ISEE Middle Level Math Exercise Book

2022

A Comprehensive Workbook

+ ISEE Middle Level Math Practice Tests

By

Reza Nazari

All inquiries should be addressed to:
info@effortlessMath.com
www.EffortlessMath.com

ISBN: 978-1-63719-219-1

Published by: **Effortless Math Education Inc.**

For Online Math Practice Visit www.EffortlessMath.com

Welcome to
ISEE Middle Level Math Prep
2022

Thank you for choosing Effortless Math for your ISEE Middle Level Math test preparation and congratulations on making the decision to take the ISEE Middle Level test! It's a remarkable move you are taking, one that shouldn't be diminished in any capacity.

That's why you need to use every tool possible to ensure you succeed on the test with the highest possible score, and this extensive math

If math has never been a strong subject for you, don't worry! This book along with our online ISEE Middle Level Math resources will help you prepare for (and even ACE) the ISEE Middle Level Math test. As test day draws nearer, effective preparation becomes increasingly more important. Thankfully, you have this comprehensive workbook to help you get ready for the test. With this book and Effortless Math online resources, you can feel confident that you will be more than ready for the ISEE Middle Level Math test when the time comes.

First and foremost, it is important to note that this book is a workbook and not a textbook. Every lesson of this practice book was carefully developed to ensure that you are making the most effective use of your time while preparing for the test. This up-to-date book reflects the 2022 test guidelines and will put you on the right track to hone your math skills, overcome exam anxiety, and boost your confidence, so that you can have your best to succeed on the ISEE Middle Level Math test.

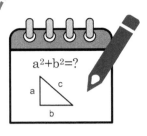

a²+b²=?

This exercise book will:

☑ Explain the format of the ISEE Middle Level Math test.

☑ Describe specific test-taking strategies that you can use on the test.

☑ Provide ISEE Middle Level Math test-taking tips.

☑ Help you identify the areas in which you need to concentrate your study time.

☑ Offer exercises that help you develop the basic math skills you will learn in each section.

☑ Give **2 realistic and full-length practice tests** (featuring new question types) with detailed answers to help you measure your exam readiness and build confidence.

This resource contains comprehensive practice questions and exercises that you will need to prepare for the ISEE Middle Level Math test. You'll get numerous skill building exercises as well as tips and techniques on how to prepare for your ISEE Middle Level math test.

In addition, in the following pages you'll find:

➢ **How to Use This Book Effectively** – This section provides you with step-by-step instructions on how to get the most out of this comprehensive study guide.

➢ **How to study for the ISEE Middle Level Math Test** – A six-step study program has been developed to help you make the best use of this book and prepare for your ISEE Middle Level Math test. Here you'll find tips and strategies to guide your study program and help you understand ISEE Middle Level Math and how to ace the test.

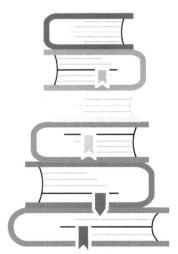

➤ **ISEE Middle Level Math Review** – Learn everything you need to know about the ISEE Middle Level Math test.

➤ **ISEE Middle Level Math Test-Taking Strategies** – Learn how to effectively put these recommended test-taking techniques into use for improving your ISEE Middle Level Math score.

➤ **Test Day Tips** – Review these tips to make sure you will do your best when the big day comes.

Effortless Math's ISEE Middle Level Online Center

Effortless Math Online ISEE Middle Level Center offers a complete study program, including the following:

✓ Step-by-step instructions on how to prepare for the ISEE Middle Level Math test

✓ Numerous ISEE Middle Level Math worksheets to help you measure your math skills

✓ Complete list of ISEE Middle Level Math formulas

✓ Video lessons for all ISEE Middle Level Math topics

✓ Full-length ISEE Middle Level Math practice tests

✓ And much more…

No Registration Required.

Visit **EffortlessMath.com/ISEEMiddle** to find your online ISEE Middle Level Math resources.

How to Use This Book Effectively

Look no further when you need a study program to improve your math skills to succeed on the math portion of the ISEE Middle Level test. Each chapter of this comprehensive workbook will provide you with the knowledge, tools, and understanding needed for every topic covered on the test.

It's imperative that you understand each topic before moving onto another one, as that's the way to guarantee your success. You can use Effortless Math online course (a free course) to find examples and a step-by-step guide of every math concept in this workbook to better understand the content that will be on the test. To get the best possible results from this book:

➢ **Begin studying long before your test date**. This provides you ample time to learn the different math concepts. The earlier you begin studying for the test, the sharper your skills will be. Do not procrastinate! Provide yourself with plenty of time to learn the concepts and feel comfortable that you understand them when your test date arrives.

➢ **Practice consistently**. Study ISEE Middle Level Math concepts at least 20 to 30 minutes a day. Remember, slow and steady wins the race, which can be applied to preparing for the ISEE Middle Level Math test. Instead of cramming to tackle everything at once, be patient and learn the math topics in short bursts.

➢ Whenever you get a math problem wrong, **mark it off, and review it later** to make sure you understand the concept.

➢ Start each session by **looking over the previous material.**

➢ Once you've reviewed the book's exercises, **take a practice test at the back of the book** to gauge your level of readiness. Then, review your results. Read detailed answers and solutions for each question you missed.

➢ **Take another practice test** to get an idea of how ready you are to take the actual exam. Taking the practice tests will give you the confidence you need on test day. Simulate the ISEE Middle Level testing environment by sitting in a quiet room free from distraction. Make sure to clock yourself with a timer.

How to Study for the ISEE Middle Level Math Test

Studying for the ISEE Middle Level Math test can be a really daunting and boring task. What's the best way to go about it? Is there a certain study method that works better than others? Well, studying for the ISEE Middle Level Math can be done effectively. The following six-step program has been designed to make preparing for the ISEE Middle Level Math test more efficient and less overwhelming.

Step **1** - Create a study plan
Step **2** - Choose your study resources
Step **3** - Review, Learn, Practice
Step **4** - Learn and practice test-taking strategies
Step **5** - Learn the ISEE Middle Level Test format and take practice tests
Step **6** - Analyze your performance

STEP 1: Create a Study Plan

It's always easier to get things done when you have a plan. Creating a study plan for the ISEE Middle Level Math test can help you to stay on track with your studies. It's important to sit down and prepare a study plan with what works with your life, school, and any other obligations you may have. Devote enough time each day to studying. It's also a  great idea to break down each section of the exam into blocks and study one concept at a time.

It's important to understand that there is no "right" way to create a study plan. Your study plan will be personalized based on your specific needs and learning style. Follow these guidelines to create an effective study plan for your ISEE Middle Level Math test:

★ **Analyze your learning style and study habits** – Everyone has a different learning style. It is essential to embrace your individuality and the unique way you learn. Think about what works and what doesn't work for you. Do you prefer ISEE Middle Level Math prep books or a combination of textbooks and

 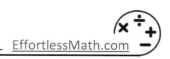

video lessons? Does it work better for you if you study every night for thirty minutes or is it more effective to study in the morning before going to school?

★ **Evaluate your schedule** – Review your current schedule and find out how much time you can consistently devote to ISEE Middle Level Math study.

★ **Develop a schedule** – Now it's time to add your study schedule to your calendar like any other obligation. Schedule time for study, practice, and review. Plan out which topic you will study on which day to ensure that you're devoting enough time to each concept. Develop a study plan that is mindful, realistic, and flexible.

★ **Stick to your schedule** – A study plan is only effective when it is followed consistently. You should try to develop a study plan that you can follow for the length of your study program.

★ **Evaluate your study plan and adjust as needed** – Sometimes you need to adjust your plan when you have new commitments. Check in with yourself regularly to make sure that you're not falling behind in your study plan. Remember, the most important thing is sticking to your plan. Your study plan is all about helping you be more productive. If you find that your study plan is not as effective as you want, don't get discouraged. It's okay to make changes as you figure out what works best for you.

STEP 2: Choose Your Study Resources

There are numerous textbooks and online resources available for the ISEE Middle Level Math test, and it may not be clear where to begin. Don't worry! This exercise book reviews all ISEE Middle Level Math concepts and topics. In addition to the book content, you can also use Effortless Math's online resources. (video lessons, worksheets, formulas, etc.) On

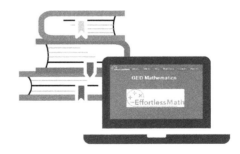

each page, there is a link (and a QR code) to an online webpage which provides a comprehensive review of the topic, step-by-step instruction, video tutorial, and numerous examples and exercises to help you fully understand the concept.

Simply visit <u>EffortlessMath.com/ISEEMiddle</u> to find your online ISEE Middle Level Math resources.

STEP 3: Review, Learn, Practice

This ISEE Middle Level Math exercise book breaks down each subject into specific skills or content areas. For instance, the percent concept is separated into different topics–percent calculation, percent increase and decrease, percent problems, etc. Use this book to help you go over all key math concepts and topics on the ISEE Middle Level Math test.

As you review each topic, take notes or highlight the concepts you would like to go over again in the future. If you're unfamiliar with a topic or something is difficult for you, use the link (or the QR code) at the top of the page to find the webpage that provides more instruction about that topic. For each math topic, plenty of instructions, step-by-step guides, and examples are provided to ensure you get a good grasp of the material.

Quickly review the topics you do understand to get a brush-up of the material. Be sure to do the practice questions provided at the end of every chapter to measure your understanding of the concepts.

STEP 4: Learn and Practice Test-taking Strategies

In the following sections, you will find important test-taking strategies and tips that can help you earn extra points. You'll learn how to think strategically and when to guess if you don't know the answer to a question. Using ISEE Middle Level Math test-taking strategies and tips can help you raise your score and do well on the test. Apply test taking strategies on the practice tests to help you boost your confidence.

STEP 5: Learn the ISEE Middle Level Test Format and Take Practice Tests

The ISEE Middle Level Test Review section provides information about the structure of the ISEE Middle Level test. Read this section to learn more about the ISEE Middle Level test structure, different test sections, the number of questions in each section, and the section time limits. When you have a prior  understanding of the test format and different types of ISEE Middle Level Math questions, you'll feel more confident when you take the actual exam.

Once you have read through the instructions and lessons and feel like you are ready to go — take advantage of both of the full-length ISEE Middle Level Math practice tests available in this exercise book. Use the practice tests to sharpen your skills and build confidence.

The ISEE Middle Level Math practice tests offered at the end of the book are formatted similarly to the actual ISEE Middle Level Math test. When you take each practice test, try to simulate actual testing conditions. To take the practice tests, sit in a quiet space, time yourself, and work through as many of the questions as time allows. The practice tests are followed by detailed answer explanations to help you find your weak areas, learn from your mistakes, and raise your ISEE Middle Level Math score.

STEP 6: Analyze Your Performance

After taking the practice tests, look over the answer keys and explanations to learn which questions you answered correctly and which you did not. Never be discouraged if you make a few mistakes. See them as a learning opportunity. This will highlight your strengths and weaknesses.

You can use the results to determine if you need additional practice or if you are ready to take the actual ISEE Middle Level Math test.

Looking for more?

Visit EffortlessMath.com/ISEEMiddle to find hundreds of ISEE Middle Level Math worksheets, video tutorials, practice tests, ISEE Middle Level Math formulas, and much more.

Or scan this QR code.

No Registration Required.

ISEE Middle Level Test Review

The Independent School Entrance Exam (ISEE) is a standardized test developed by the Educational Records Bureau for its member schools as part of their admission process.

There are currently four Levels of the ISEE:

- ✓ Primary Level (entering Grades 2 - 4)
- ✓ Lower Level (entering Grades 5 and 6)
- ✓ Middle Level (entering Grades 7 and 8)
- ✓ Upper Level (entering Grades 9 - 12)

There are five sections on the ISEE Middle Level Test:

- o Verbal Reasoning
- o Quantitative Reasoning
- o Reading Comprehension
- o Mathematics Achievement
- o and a 30-minute essay

ISEE Middle Level tests use a multiple-choice format and contain two Mathematics sections:

Quantitative Reasoning

There are 37 questions in the Quantitative Reasoning section and students have 35 minutes to answer the questions. This section contains word problems and quantitative comparisons. The word problems require either no calculation or simple calculation. The quantitative comparison items present two quantities, (A) and (B), and the student needs to select one of the following four answer choices:

(A) The quantity in Column A is greater.

(B) The quantity in Column B is greater.

(C) The two quantities are equal.

(D) The relationship cannot be determined from the information given.

Mathematics Achievement

There are 47 questions in the Mathematics Achievement section and students have 40 minutes to answer the questions. Mathematics Achievement measures students' knowledge of Mathematics requiring one or more steps in calculating the answer.

ISEE Middle Level Math Test-Taking Strategies

Here are some test-taking strategies that you can use to maximize your performance and results on the ISEE Middle Level Math test.

#1: USE THIS APPROACH TO ANSWER EVERY ISEE MIDDLE LEVEL MATH QUESTION

1) Review the question to identify keywords and important information.
2) Translate the keywords into math operations so you can solve the problem.
3) Review the answer choices. What are the differences between answer choices?
4) Draw or label a diagram if needed.
5) Try to find patterns.
6) Find the right method to answer the question. Use straightforward math, plug in numbers, or test the answer choices (backsolving).
7) Double-check your work.

#2: USE EDUCATED GUESSING

This approach is applicable to the problems you understand to some degree but cannot solve using straightforward math. In such cases, try to filter out as many answer choices as possible before picking an answer. In cases where you don't have a clue about what a certain problem entails, don't waste any time trying to eliminate answer choices. Just choose one randomly before moving onto the next question.

As you can ascertain, direct solutions are the most optimal approach. Carefully read through the question, determine what the solution is using the math you have learned before, then coordinate the answer with one of the choices available to you. Are you stumped? Make your best guess, then move on.

Don't leave any fields empty! Even if you're unable to work out a problem, strive to answer it. Take a guess if you have to. You will not lose points by getting an answer wrong, though you may gain a point by getting it correct!

#3 : BALLPARK

A ballpark answer is a rough approximation. When we become overwhelmed by calculations and figures, we end up making silly mistakes. A decimal that is moved by one unit can change an answer from right to wrong, regardless of the number of steps that you went through to get it. That's where ballparking can play a big part.

If you think you know what the correct answer may be (even if it's just a ballpark answer), you'll usually have the ability to eliminate a couple of choices. While answer choices are usually based on the average student error and/or values that are closely tied, you will still be able to weed out choices that are way far afield. Try to find answers that aren't in the proverbial ballpark when you're looking for a wrong answer on a multiple-choice question. This is an optimal approach to eliminating answers to a problem.

#4 : BACKSOLVING

A majority of questions on the ISEE Middle Level Math test will be in multiple-choice format. Many test-takers prefer multiple-choice questions, as at least the answer is right there. You'll typically have four answers to pick from. You simply need to figure out which one is correct. Usually, the best way to go about doing so is "backsolving."

As mentioned earlier, direct solutions are the most optimal approach to answering a question. Carefully read through a problem, calculate a solution, then correspond the answer with one of the choices displayed in front of you. If you can't calculate a solution, your next best approach involves "backsolving."

When backsolving a problem, contrast one of your answer options against the problem you are asked, then see which of them is most relevant. More often than not, answer choices are listed in ascending or descending order. In such cases, try out the choices B or C. If it's not correct, you can go either down or up from there.

#5 : PLUGGING IN NUMBERS

"Plugging in numbers" is a strategy that can be applied to a wide range of different math problems on the ISEE Middle Level Math test. This approach is typically used to simplify a challenging question so that it is more understandable. By using the strategy carefully, you can find the answer without too much trouble.

The concept is fairly straightforward—replace unknown variables in a problem with certain values. When selecting a number, consider the following:

- Choose a number that's basic (just not too basic). Generally, you should avoid choosing 1 (or even 0). A decent choice is 2.

- Try not to choose a number that is displayed in the problem.

- Make sure you keep your numbers different if you need to choose at least two of them.

- More often than not, choosing numbers merely lets you filter out some of your answer choices. As such, don't just go with the first choice that gives you the right answer.

- If several answers seem correct, then you'll need to choose another value and try again. This time, though, you'll just need to check choices that haven't been eliminated yet.

- If your question contains fractions, then a potential right answer may involve either an LCD (least common denominator) or an LCD multiple.

- 100 is the number you should choose when you are dealing with problems involving percentages.

ISEE Middle Level Math – Test Day Tips

After practicing and reviewing all the math concepts you've been taught, and taking some ISEE Middle Level mathematics practice tests, you'll be prepared for test day. Consider the following tips to be extra-ready come test time.

Before Your Test

What to do the night before:

- **Relax!** One day before your test, study lightly or skip studying altogether. You shouldn't attempt to learn something new, either. There are plenty of reasons why studying the evening before a big test can work against you. Put it this way–a marathoner wouldn't go out for a sprint before the day of a big race. Mental marathoners–such as yourself–should not study for any more than one hour 24 hours before a ISEE Middle Level test. That's because your brain requires some rest to be at its best. The night before your exam, spend some time with family or friends, or read a book.

- **Avoid bright screens** - You'll have to get some good shuteye the night before your test. Bright screens (such as the ones coming from your laptop, TV, or mobile device) should be avoided altogether. Staring at such a screen will keep your brain up, making it hard to drift asleep at a reasonable hour.

- **Make sure your dinner is healthy** - The meal that you have for dinner should be nutritious. Be sure to drink plenty of water as well. Load up on your complex carbohydrates, much like a marathon runner would do. Pasta, rice, and potatoes are ideal options here, as are vegetables and protein sources.

- **Get your bag ready for test day** - The night prior to your test, pack your bag with your stationery, admissions pass, ID, and any other gear that you need. Keep the bag right by your front door.

- **Make plans to reach the testing site** - Before going to sleep, ensure that you understand precisely how you will arrive at the site of the test. If parking is something you'll have to find first, plan for it. If you're dependent on public transit, then review the schedule. You should also make sure that the train/bus/subway/streetcar you use will be running. Find out about road closures as well. If a parent or friend is accompanying you, ensure that they understand what steps they have to take as well.

The Day of the Test

- **Get up reasonably early, but not too early.**

- **Have breakfast** - Breakfast improves your concentration, memory, and mood. As such, make sure the breakfast that you eat in the morning is healthy. The last thing you want to be is distracted by a grumbling tummy. If it's not your own stomach making those noises, another test taker close to you might be instead. Prevent discomfort or embarrassment by consuming a healthy breakfast. Bring a snack with you if you think you'll need it.

- **Follow your daily routine** - Do you watch TV each morning while getting ready for the day? Don't break your usual habits on the day of the test. Likewise, if coffee isn't something you drink in the morning, then don't take up the habit hours before your test. Routine consistency lets you concentrate on the main objective—doing the best you can on your test.

- **Wear layers** - Dress yourself up in comfortable layers. You should be ready for any kind of internal temperature. If it gets too warm during the test, take a layer off.

- **Get there on time** - The last thing you want to do is get to the test site late. Rather, you should be there 45 minutes prior to the start of the test. Upon your arrival, try not to hang out with anybody who is nervous. Any anxious energy they exhibit shouldn't influence you.

- **Leave the books at home** - No books should be brought to the test site. If you start developing anxiety before the test, books could encourage you to do some last-minute studying, which will only hinder you. Keep the books far away—better yet, leave them at home.

- **Make your voice heard** - If something is off, speak to a proctor. If medical attention is needed or if you'll require anything, consult the proctor prior to the start of the test. Any doubts you have should be clarified. You should be entering the test site with a state of mind that is completely clear.

- **Have faith in yourself** - When you feel confident, you will be able to perform at your best. When you are waiting for the test to begin, envision yourself receiving an outstanding result. Try to see yourself as someone who knows all the answers, no matter what the questions are. A lot of athletes tend to use this technique—particularly before a big competition. Your expectations will be reflected by your performance.

During your test

- **Be calm and breathe deeply** - You need to relax before the test, and some deep breathing will go a long way to help you do that. Be confident and calm. You got this. Everybody feels a little stressed out just before an evaluation of any kind is set to begin. Learn some effective breathing exercises. Spend a minute meditating before the test starts. Filter out any negative thoughts you have. Exhibit confidence when having such thoughts.

- **Concentrate on the test** - Refrain from comparing yourself to anyone else. You shouldn't be distracted by the people near you or random noise. Concentrate exclusively on the test. If you find yourself irritated by surrounding noises, earplugs can be used to block sounds off close to you. Don't forget—the test is going to last several hours if you're taking more than one subject of the test. Some of that time will be dedicated to brief sections. Concentrate on the specific section you are working on during a particular moment. Do not let your mind wander off to upcoming or previous sections.

- **Skip challenging questions** - Optimize your time when taking the test. Lingering on a single question for too long will work against you. If you don't know what the answer is to a certain question, use your best guess, and mark the question so you can review it later on. There is no need to spend time attempting to solve something you aren't sure about. That time would be better served handling the questions you can actually answer well. You will not be penalized for getting the wrong answer on a test like this.

- **Try to answer each question individually** - Focus only on the question you are working on. Use one of the test-taking strategies to solve the problem. If you aren't able to come up with an answer, don't get frustrated. Simply skip that question, then move onto the next one.

- **Don't forget to breathe!** Whenever you notice your mind wandering, your stress levels boosting, or frustration brewing, take a thirty-second break. Shut your eyes, drop your pencil, breathe deeply, and let your shoulders relax. You will end up being more productive when you allow yourself to relax for a moment.

- **Review your answer.** If you still have time at the end of the test, don't waste it. Go back and check over your answers. It is worth going through the test from start to finish to ensure that you didn't make a sloppy mistake somewhere.

- **Optimize your breaks** - When break time comes, use the restroom, have a snack, and reactivate your energy for the subsequent section. Doing some stretches can help stimulate your blood flow.

After your test

- **Take it easy** - You will need to set some time aside to relax and decompress once the test has concluded. There is no need to stress yourself out about what you could've said, or what you may have done wrong. At this point, there's nothing you can do about it. Your energy and time would be better spent on something that will bring you happiness for the remainder of your day.

Contents

Chapter 1: Fractions and Mixed Numbers

Math Topics that you'll learn in this Chapter:

- ✓ Simplifying Fractions
- ✓ Adding and Subtracting Fractions
- ✓ Multiplying and Dividing Fractions
- ✓ Adding Mixed Numbers
- ✓ Subtracting Mixed Numbers
- ✓ Multiplying Mixed Numbers
- ✓ Dividing Mixed Numbers

24

Simplifying Fractions

Simplify each fraction to its lowest terms.

1) $\frac{9}{18} = \frac{1}{2}$

2) $\frac{8}{10} = \frac{4}{5}$

3) $\frac{6}{8} = \frac{3}{4}$

4) $\frac{5}{20} = \frac{1}{4}$

5) $\frac{18}{24} = \frac{3}{4}$

6) $\frac{6}{9} = \frac{2}{3}$

7) $\frac{12}{15} = \frac{4}{5}$

8) $\frac{4}{16} = \frac{1}{4}$

9) $\frac{18}{36} = \frac{1}{2}$

10) $\frac{6}{42} = \frac{1}{7}$

11) $\frac{13}{39} = \frac{1}{3}$

12) $\frac{21}{28} = \frac{3}{4}$

13) $\frac{63}{77} =$

14) $\frac{36}{40} =$

15) $\frac{21}{63} =$

16) $\frac{30}{84} =$

17) $\frac{50}{125} =$

18) $\frac{72}{108} =$

19) $\frac{49}{112} =$

20) $\frac{240}{320} =$

21) $\frac{120}{150} =$

Solve each problem.

22) Which of the following fractions equal to $\frac{4}{5}$? _____

     Ⓐ $\frac{64}{75}$ B. $\frac{92}{115}$ C. $\frac{60}{85}$ D. $\frac{160}{220}$

23) Which of the following fractions equal to $\frac{3}{7}$? _____

     A. $\frac{63}{147}$ B. $\frac{75}{182}$ C. $\frac{54}{140}$ D. $\frac{39}{98}$

24) Which of the following fractions equal to $\frac{2}{9}$? _____

     A. $\frac{84}{386}$ B. $\frac{52}{234}$ C. $\frac{96}{450}$ D. $\frac{112}{522}$

Adding and Subtracting Fractions

✎ Find the sum.

1) $\frac{1}{3} + \frac{2}{3} =$ $\frac{3}{3} = 1$

2) $\frac{1}{2} + \frac{1}{3} =$ $\frac{5}{6}$

3) $\frac{2}{5} + \frac{1}{2} =$ $\frac{9}{10}$

4) $\frac{3}{7} + \frac{2}{3} =$ $\frac{23}{21} = 1\frac{2}{21}$

5) $\frac{3}{4} + \frac{2}{5} =$ $\frac{23}{20} = 1\frac{3}{20}$

6) $\frac{3}{5} + \frac{1}{5} =$ $\frac{4}{5}$

7) $\frac{5}{9} + \frac{1}{2} =$ $\frac{14}{18} = 1\frac{1}{18}$

8) $\frac{3}{5} + \frac{3}{8} =$

9) $\frac{5}{9} + \frac{3}{7} =$

10) $\frac{5}{11} + \frac{1}{4} =$

11) $\frac{3}{7} + \frac{1}{6} =$

12) $\frac{3}{14} + \frac{3}{4} =$

✎ Find the difference.

13) $\frac{1}{2} - \frac{1}{3} =$ $\frac{1}{6}$

14) $\frac{4}{5} - \frac{2}{3} =$ $\frac{22}{15} = 1\frac{7}{15}$

15) $\frac{2}{3} - \frac{1}{6} =$ $\frac{3}{6}$

16) $\frac{3}{5} - \frac{1}{2} =$

17) $\frac{8}{9} - \frac{2}{5} =$

18) $\frac{4}{7} - \frac{1}{9} =$

19) $\frac{2}{5} - \frac{1}{4} =$

20) $\frac{5}{8} - \frac{2}{6} =$

21) $\frac{4}{15} - \frac{1}{10} =$

22) $\frac{7}{20} - \frac{1}{5} =$

23) $\frac{3}{18} - \frac{1}{12} =$

24) $\frac{9}{24} - \frac{3}{16} =$

25) $\frac{3}{7} - \frac{2}{5} =$

26) $\frac{5}{9} - \frac{1}{6} =$

27) $\frac{2}{5} - \frac{1}{10} =$

28) $\frac{5}{12} - \frac{2}{9} =$

29) $\frac{2}{13} - \frac{3}{7} =$

30) $\frac{4}{11} - \frac{5}{8} =$

Multiplying and Dividing Fractions

✎ *Find the value of each expression in lowest terms.*

1) $\frac{1}{2} \times \frac{3}{4} =$

2) $\frac{3}{5} \times \frac{2}{3} =$

3) $\frac{1}{4} \times \frac{2}{5} =$

4) $\frac{1}{6} \times \frac{4}{5} =$

5) $\frac{1}{5} \times \frac{1}{4} =$

6) $\frac{2}{5} \times \frac{1}{2} =$

7) $\frac{7}{9} \times \frac{1}{3} =$

8) $\frac{5}{7} \times \frac{3}{8} =$

9) $\frac{8}{9} \times \frac{6}{7} =$

10) $\frac{5}{6} \times \frac{3}{5} =$

11) $\frac{3}{8} \times \frac{1}{9} =$

12) $\frac{1}{12} \times \frac{3}{7} =$

✎ *Find the value of each expression in lowest terms.*

13) $\frac{1}{2} \div \frac{1}{4} =$

14) $\frac{1}{3} \div \frac{1}{2} =$

15) $\frac{2}{5} \div \frac{1}{3} =$

16) $\frac{1}{4} \div \frac{2}{3} =$

17) $\frac{1}{5} \div \frac{3}{10} =$

18) $\frac{2}{7} \div \frac{1}{3} =$

19) $\frac{3}{5} \div \frac{5}{9} =$

20) $\frac{2}{23} \div \frac{2}{9} =$

21) $\frac{4}{13} \div \frac{1}{4} =$

22) $\frac{9}{14} \div \frac{3}{7} =$

23) $\frac{8}{15} \div \frac{2}{5} =$

24) $\frac{2}{9} \div \frac{7}{11} =$

25) $\frac{2}{5} \div \frac{3}{4} =$

26) $\frac{4}{11} \div \frac{2}{5} =$

27) $\frac{2}{15} \div \frac{5}{8} =$

28) $\frac{3}{10} \div \frac{2}{5} =$

29) $\frac{4}{5} \div \frac{3}{7} =$

30) $\frac{2}{11} \div \frac{3}{5} =$

Adding Mixed Numbers

✎ *Solve and write the answer in lowest terms*

1) $1\frac{1}{5} + 2\frac{2}{5} =$

2) $1\frac{1}{2} + 4\frac{5}{6} =$

3) $2\frac{4}{5} + 2\frac{3}{10} =$

4) $3\frac{1}{6} + 2\frac{2}{5} =$

5) $1\frac{5}{6} + 1\frac{2}{5} =$

6) $3\frac{5}{7} + 1\frac{2}{9} =$

7) $3\frac{5}{8} + 2\frac{1}{3} =$

8) $1\frac{6}{7} + 3\frac{2}{9} =$

9) $2\frac{5}{9} + 1\frac{1}{4} =$

10) $3\frac{7}{9} + 2\frac{5}{6} =$

11) $2\frac{1}{10} + 2\frac{2}{5} =$

12) $1\frac{3}{10} + 3\frac{4}{5} =$

13) $3\frac{1}{12} + 2\frac{1}{3} =$

14) $5\frac{1}{11} + 1\frac{1}{2} =$

15) $3\frac{1}{21} + 2\frac{2}{3} =$

16) $4\frac{1}{24} + 1\frac{5}{8} =$

17) $2\frac{1}{25} + 3\frac{3}{5} =$

18) $3\frac{1}{15} + 2\frac{2}{10} =$

19) $5\frac{6}{7} + 2\frac{1}{3} =$

20) $2\frac{1}{8} + 3\frac{3}{4} =$

21) $2\frac{5}{7} + 2\frac{2}{21} =$

22) $4\frac{1}{6} + 1\frac{4}{5} =$

23) $2\frac{1}{7} + 2\frac{3}{8} =$

24) $3\frac{1}{4} + 2\frac{2}{3} =$

25) $1\frac{1}{13} + 2\frac{3}{4} =$

26) $3\frac{2}{35} + 2\frac{5}{7} =$

Subtracting Mixed Numbers

✍ *Solve and write the answer in lowest terms.*

1) $5\frac{2}{9} - 2\frac{1}{9} =$

2) $6\frac{2}{7} - 2\frac{1}{3} =$

3) $5\frac{3}{8} - 2\frac{3}{4} =$

4) $7\frac{2}{5} - 3\frac{1}{10} =$

5) $9\frac{5}{7} - 7\frac{4}{21} =$

6) $11\frac{7}{12} - 9\frac{5}{6} =$

7) $9\frac{5}{9} - 8\frac{1}{8} =$

8) $13\frac{7}{9} - 11\frac{3}{7} =$

9) $8\frac{7}{12} - 7\frac{3}{8} =$

10) $11\frac{5}{9} - 9\frac{1}{4} =$

11) $6\frac{5}{6} - 2\frac{2}{9} =$

12) $5\frac{7}{8} - 4\frac{1}{3} =$

13) $9\frac{5}{8} - 8\frac{1}{2} =$

14) $4\frac{9}{16} - 2\frac{1}{4} =$

15) $3\frac{2}{3} - 1\frac{2}{15} =$

16) $5\frac{1}{2} - 4\frac{2}{17} =$

17) $5\frac{6}{7} - 2\frac{1}{3} =$

18) $3\frac{3}{7} - 2\frac{2}{21} =$

19) $7\frac{3}{10} - 5\frac{2}{15} =$

20) $4\frac{5}{6} - 2\frac{2}{9} =$

21) $6\frac{3}{7} - 2\frac{2}{9} =$

22) $7\frac{4}{5} - 6\frac{3}{7} =$

23) $12\frac{3}{7} - 8\frac{1}{3} =$

24) $5\frac{4}{9} - 2\frac{5}{6} =$

25) $10\frac{1}{28} - 7\frac{3}{4} =$

26) $11\frac{5}{12} - 7\frac{5}{48} =$

Multiplying Mixed Numbers

✎ *Solve and write the answer in lowest terms*

1) $1\frac{1}{6} \times 1\frac{3}{7} =$

2) $5\frac{1}{6} \times 2\frac{1}{4} =$

3) $3\frac{3}{7} \times 1\frac{2}{9} =$

4) $3\frac{3}{8} \times 3\frac{1}{6} =$

5) $1\frac{1}{2} \times 5\frac{2}{3} =$

6) $3\frac{1}{2} \times 6\frac{2}{3} =$

7) $9\frac{1}{2} \times 2\frac{1}{6} =$

8) $2\frac{5}{8} \times 8\frac{3}{5} =$

9) $3\frac{4}{5} \times 4\frac{2}{3} =$

10) $5\frac{1}{3} \times 2\frac{2}{7} =$

11) $6\frac{1}{3} \times 3\frac{3}{4} =$

12) $7\frac{2}{3} \times 1\frac{8}{9} =$

13) $8\frac{1}{2} \times 2\frac{1}{6} =$

14) $4\frac{1}{5} \times 8\frac{2}{3} =$

15) $3\frac{1}{8} \times 5\frac{2}{3} =$

16) $2\frac{2}{7} \times 6\frac{2}{5} =$

17) $2\frac{3}{8} \times 7\frac{2}{3} =$

18) $1\frac{7}{8} \times 8\frac{2}{3} =$

19) $9\frac{1}{2} \times 3\frac{1}{5} =$

20) $2\frac{5}{8} \times 4\frac{1}{3} =$

21) $6\frac{1}{3} \times 3\frac{2}{5} =$

22) $5\frac{3}{4} \times 2\frac{2}{7} =$

23) $8\frac{1}{6} \times 2\frac{2}{7} =$

24) $4\frac{1}{6} \times 7\frac{1}{5} =$

25) $2\frac{1}{5} \times 2\frac{5}{8} =$

26) $6\frac{2}{3} \times 4\frac{3}{5} =$

bit.ly/3aPy7XJ

Find more at

Dividing Mixed Numbers

✎ *Solve and write the answer in lowest terms*

1) $6\frac{1}{2} \div 4\frac{2}{5} =$

2) $1\frac{3}{8} \div 1\frac{1}{4} =$

3) $6\frac{2}{5} \div 2\frac{4}{5} =$

4) $7\frac{1}{3} \div 6\frac{3}{4} =$

5) $7\frac{2}{5} \div 3\frac{3}{4} =$

6) $2\frac{4}{5} \div 3\frac{2}{3} =$

7) $8\frac{3}{5} \div 4\frac{3}{4} =$

8) $6\frac{3}{4} \div 2\frac{2}{9} =$

9) $5\frac{2}{7} \div 2\frac{2}{9} =$

10) $2\frac{2}{5} \div 3\frac{3}{5} =$

11) $4\frac{3}{7} \div 1\frac{7}{8} =$

12) $2\frac{5}{7} \div 2\frac{4}{5} =$

13) $8\frac{3}{5} \div 6\frac{1}{5} =$

14) $2\frac{5}{8} \div 1\frac{8}{9} =$

15) $5\frac{6}{7} \div 2\frac{3}{4} =$

16) $1\frac{3}{5} \div 2\frac{3}{8} =$

17) $5\frac{3}{4} \div 3\frac{2}{5} =$

18) $2\frac{3}{4} \div 3\frac{1}{5} =$

19) $3\frac{2}{3} \div 1\frac{2}{5} =$

20) $4\frac{1}{4} \div 2\frac{2}{3} =$

21) $3\frac{5}{6} \div 2\frac{4}{5} =$

22) $2\frac{1}{8} \div 1\frac{3}{4} =$

23) $5\frac{1}{2} \div 4\frac{2}{5} =$

24) $6\frac{3}{7} \div 2\frac{1}{7} =$

25) $3\frac{3}{6} \div 1\frac{5}{7} =$

26) $4\frac{4}{9} \div 4\frac{2}{3} =$

Answers – Chapter 1

Simplifying Fractions

1) $\frac{1}{2}$

2) $\frac{4}{5}$

3) $\frac{3}{4}$

4) $\frac{1}{4}$

5) $\frac{3}{4}$

6) $\frac{2}{3}$

7) $\frac{4}{5}$

8) $\frac{1}{4}$

9) $\frac{1}{2}$

10) $\frac{1}{7}$

11) $\frac{1}{3}$

12) $\frac{3}{4}$

13) $\frac{9}{11}$

14) $\frac{9}{10}$

15) $\frac{1}{3}$

16) $\frac{5}{14}$

17) $\frac{2}{5}$

18) $\frac{2}{3}$

19) $\frac{7}{16}$

20) $\frac{3}{4}$

21) $\frac{4}{5}$

22) B

23) A

24) B

Adding and Subtracting Fractions

1) $\frac{3}{3} = 1$

2) $\frac{5}{6}$

3) $\frac{9}{10}$

4) $\frac{23}{21}$

5) $\frac{23}{20}$

6) $\frac{4}{5}$

7) $\frac{19}{18}$

8) $\frac{39}{40}$

9) $\frac{62}{63}$

10) $\frac{31}{44}$

11) $\frac{25}{42}$

12) $\frac{27}{28}$

13) $\frac{1}{6}$

14) $\frac{2}{15}$

15) $\frac{1}{2}$

16) $\frac{1}{10}$

17) $\frac{22}{45}$

18) $\frac{29}{63}$

19) $\frac{3}{20}$

20) $\frac{7}{24}$

21) $\frac{1}{6}$

22) $\frac{3}{20}$

23) $\frac{1}{12}$

24) $\frac{3}{16}$

25) $\frac{1}{35}$

26) $\frac{7}{18}$

27) $\frac{3}{10}$

28) $\frac{7}{36}$

29) $-\frac{25}{91}$

30) $-\frac{23}{88}$

Multiplying and Dividing Fractions

1) $\frac{3}{8}$

2) $\frac{2}{5}$

3) $\frac{1}{10}$

4) $\frac{2}{15}$

5) $\frac{1}{20}$

6) $\frac{1}{5}$

7) $\frac{7}{27}$

8) $\frac{15}{56}$

9) $\frac{16}{21}$

Effortless Math Education

10) $\frac{1}{2}$

11) $\frac{1}{24}$

12) $\frac{1}{28}$

13) 2

14) $\frac{2}{3}$

15) $\frac{6}{5}$

16) $\frac{3}{8}$

17) $\frac{2}{3}$

18) $\frac{6}{7}$

19) $\frac{27}{25}$

20) $\frac{9}{23}$

21) $\frac{16}{13}$

22) $\frac{3}{2}$

23) $\frac{4}{3}$

24) $\frac{22}{63}$

25) $\frac{8}{15}$

26) $\frac{10}{11}$

27) $\frac{16}{75}$

28) $\frac{3}{4}$

29) $\frac{28}{15}$

30) $\frac{10}{33}$

Adding Mixed Numbers

1) $3\frac{3}{5}$

2) $6\frac{1}{3}$

3) $5\frac{1}{10}$

4) $5\frac{17}{30}$

5) $3\frac{7}{30}$

6) $4\frac{59}{63}$

7) $5\frac{23}{24}$

8) $5\frac{5}{63}$

9) $3\frac{29}{36}$

10) $6\frac{11}{18}$

11) $4\frac{1}{2}$

12) $5\frac{1}{10}$

13) $5\frac{5}{12}$

14) $6\frac{13}{22}$

15) $5\frac{5}{7}$

16) $5\frac{2}{3}$

17) $5\frac{16}{25}$

18) $5\frac{4}{15}$

19) $8\frac{4}{21}$

20) $5\frac{7}{8}$

21) $4\frac{17}{21}$

22) $5\frac{29}{30}$

23) $4\frac{29}{56}$

24) $5\frac{11}{12}$

25) $3\frac{43}{52}$

26) $5\frac{27}{35}$

Subtracting Mixed Numbers

1) $3\frac{1}{9}$

2) $3\frac{20}{21}$

3) $2\frac{5}{8}$

4) $4\frac{3}{10}$

5) $2\frac{11}{21}$

6) $1\frac{3}{4}$

7) $1\frac{31}{72}$

8) $2\frac{22}{63}$

9) $1\frac{5}{24}$

10) $2\frac{11}{36}$

11) $4\frac{11}{18}$

12) $1\frac{13}{24}$

13) $1\frac{1}{8}$

14) $2\frac{5}{16}$

15) $2\frac{8}{15}$

16) $1\frac{13}{34}$

17) $3\frac{11}{21}$

18) $1\frac{1}{3}$

19) $2\frac{1}{6}$

20) $2\frac{11}{18}$

21) $4\frac{13}{63}$

22) $1\frac{13}{35}$

23) $4\frac{2}{21}$

24) $2\frac{11}{18}$

25) $2\frac{2}{7}$

26) $4\frac{5}{16}$

Multiplying Mixed Numbers

1) $1\frac{2}{3}$

2) $11\frac{5}{8}$

3) $4\frac{4}{21}$

4) $10\frac{11}{16}$

5) $8\frac{1}{2}$

6) $23\frac{1}{3}$

7) $20\frac{7}{12}$

8) $22\frac{23}{40}$

9) $17\frac{11}{15}$

10) $12\frac{4}{21}$

11) $23\frac{3}{4}$

12) $14\frac{13}{27}$

13) $18\frac{5}{12}$

14) $36\frac{2}{5}$

15) $17\frac{17}{24}$

16) $14\frac{22}{35}$

17) $18\frac{5}{24}$

18) $16\frac{1}{4}$

19) $30\frac{2}{5}$

20) $11\frac{3}{8}$

21) $21\frac{8}{15}$

22) $13\frac{1}{7}$

23) $18\frac{2}{3}$

24) 30

25) $5\frac{31}{40}$

26) $30\frac{2}{3}$

Dividing Mixed Numbers

1) $1\frac{21}{44}$

2) $1\frac{1}{10}$

3) $2\frac{2}{7}$

4) $1\frac{7}{81}$

5) $1\frac{73}{75}$

6) $\frac{42}{55}$

7) $1\frac{77}{95}$

8) $3\frac{3}{80}$

9) $2\frac{53}{140}$

10) $\frac{2}{3}$

11) $2\frac{38}{105}$

12) $\frac{95}{98}$

13) $1\frac{12}{31}$

14) $1\frac{53}{136}$

15) $2\frac{10}{77}$

16) $\frac{64}{95}$

17) $1\frac{47}{68}$

18) $\frac{55}{64}$

19) $2\frac{13}{21}$

20) $1\frac{19}{32}$

21) $1\frac{31}{84}$

22) $1\frac{3}{14}$

23) $1\frac{1}{4}$

24) 3

25) $2\frac{1}{24}$

26) $\frac{20}{21}$

Effortless
Math
Education

Chapter 2: Decimal

Math Topics that you'll learn in this Chapter:

- ✓ Comparing Decimals
- ✓ Rounding Decimals
- ✓ Adding and Subtracting Decimals
- ✓ Multiplying and Dividing Decimals

13

Comparing Decimals

✎ *Write the correct comparison symbol (>, < or =).*

1) 0.50 ☐ 0.050

2) 0.025 ☐ 0.25

3) 2.060 ☐ 2.07

4) 1.75 ☐ 1.07

5) 4.04 ☐ 0.440

6) 3.05 ☐ 3.5

7) 5.05 ☐ 5.050

8) 1.02 ☐ 1.1

9) 2.45 ☐ 2.125

10) 0.932 ☐ 0.0932

11) 3.15 ☐ 3.150

12) 0.718 ☐ 0.89

13) 7.060 ☐ 7.60

14) 3.59 ☐ 3.129

15) 4.33 ☐ 4.319

16) 2.25 ☐ 2.250

17) 1.95 ☐ 1.095

18) 8.051 ☐ 8.50

19) 1.022 ☐ 1.020

20) 3.77 ☐ 3.770

bit.ly/2WHt2Za
Find more at

EffortlessMath.com

Rounding Decimals

✏ *Round each decimal to the nearest whole number.*

1) 23.18   3) 14.45   5) 3.95

2) 8.6   4) 7.5   6) 56.7

✏ *Round each decimal to the nearest tenth.*

7) 22.652   9) 47.847   11) 16.184

8) 30.342   10) 82.88   12) 71.79

✏ *Round each decimal to the nearest hundredth.*

13) 5.439   15) 26.1855   17) 91.448

14) 12.907   16) 48.623   18) 29.354

✏ *Round each decimal to the nearest thousandth.*

19) 14.67374   21) 78.7191   23) 10.0678

20) 7.54647   22) 70.2732   24) 46.54765

Find more at   bit.ly/3mKEluf

Adding and Subtracting Decimals

✎ *Add and subtract decimals.*

1)
$$
\begin{array}{r}
31.13 \\
- \ 11.45 \\
\hline
\end{array}
$$

4)
$$
\begin{array}{r}
56.67 \\
- \ 44.39 \\
\hline
\end{array}
$$

7)
$$
\begin{array}{r}
66.24 \\
- \ 23.11 \\
\hline
\end{array}
$$

2)
$$
\begin{array}{r}
35.25 \\
+ \ 24.47 \\
\hline
\end{array}
$$

5)
$$
\begin{array}{r}
71.47 \\
+ \ 16.25 \\
\hline
\end{array}
$$

8)
$$
\begin{array}{r}
39.75 \\
+ \ 12.85 \\
\hline
\end{array}
$$

3)
$$
\begin{array}{r}
73.50 \\
+ \ 22.78 \\
\hline
\end{array}
$$

6)
$$
\begin{array}{r}
68.99 \\
- \ 53.61 \\
\hline
\end{array}
$$

9)
$$
\begin{array}{r}
229.25 \\
- \ 84.67 \\
\hline
\end{array}
$$

✎ *Find the missing number.*

10) ___ + 2.5 = 3.9

11) 1.7 + ___ = 4.98

12) 5.25 + ___ = 7

13) 6.55 − ___ = 2.45

14) ___ − 3.98 = 5.32

15) ___ − 11.67 = 14.48

16) 12.35 + ___ = 14.78

17) ___ − 23.89 = 13.90

18) ___ + 17.28 = 19.56

19) 77.90 + ___ = 102.60

Multiplying and Dividing Decimals

✎ *Find the product.*

1) $0.5 \times 0.4 =$

2) $2.5 \times 0.2 =$

3) $1.25 \times 0.5 =$

4) $0.75 \times 0.2 =$

5) $1.92 \times 0.8 =$

6) $0.55 \times 0.4 =$

7) $3.24 \times 1.2 =$

8) $12.5 \times 4.2 =$

9) $22.6 \times 8.2 =$

10) $17.2 \times 4.5 =$

11) $25.1 \times 12.5 =$

12) $33.2 \times 2.2 =$

✎ *Find the quotient.*

13) $1.67 \div 100 =$

14) $52.2 \div 1,000 =$

15) $4.2 \div 2 =$

16) $8.6 \div 0.5 =$

17) $12.6 \div 0.2 =$

18) $16.5 \div 5 =$

19) $13.25 \div 100 =$

20) $25.6 \div 0.4 =$

21) $28.24 \div 0.1 =$

22) $34.16 \div 0.25 =$

23) $44.28 \div 0.5 =$

24) $38.78 \div 0.02 =$

Answers – Chapter 2

Comparing Decimals

1) >
2) <
3) <
4) >
5) >
6) <
7) =
8) <
9) >
10) >
11) =
12) <
13) <
14) >
15) >
16) =
17) >
18) <
19) >
20) =

Rounding Decimals

1) 23
2) 9
3) 14
4) 8
5) 4
6) 57
7) 22.7
8) 30.3
9) 47.8
10) 82.9
11) 16.2
12) 71.8
13) 5.44
14) 12.91
15) 26.19
16) 48.62
17) 91.45
18) 29.35
19) 14.674
20) 7.546
21) 78.719
22) 70.273
23) 10.068
24) 46.548

Adding and Subtracting Decimals

1) 19.68
2) 59.72
3) 96.28
4) 12.28
5) 87.72
6) 15.38
7) 43.13
8) 52.60
9) 144.58
10) 1.4
11) 3.28
12) 1.75
13) 4.1
14) 9.3
15) 26.15
16) 2.43
17) 37.79
18) 2.28
19) 24.7

Multiplying and Dividing Decimals

1) 0.2
2) 0.5
3) 0.625
4) 0.15
5) 1.536
6) 0.22
7) 3.888
8) 52.5
9) 185.32
10) 77.4
11) 313.75
12) 73.04
13) 0.0167
14) 0.0522
15) 2.1
16) 17.2
17) 63
18) 3.3
19) 0.1325
20) 64
21) 282.4
22) 136.64
23) 88.56
24) 1,939

Chapter 3: Integers and Order of Operations

Math Topics that you'll learn in this Chapter:

- ✓ Adding and Subtracting Integers
- ✓ Multiplying and Dividing Integers
- ✓ Order of Operations
- ✓ Integers and Absolute Value

19

Adding and Subtracting Integers

✎ *Find each sum.*

1) $12 + (-5) =$

2) $(-14) + (-18) =$

3) $8 + (-28) =$

4) $43 + (-12) =$

5) $(-7) + (-11) + 4 =$

6) $37 + (-16) + 12 =$

7) $29 + (-21) + (-12) + 20 =$

8) $(-15) + (-25) + 18 + 25 =$

9) $30 + (-28) + (35 - 32) =$

10) $25 + (-15) + (44 - 17) =$

✎ *Find each difference.*

11) $(-12) - (-8) =$

12) $15 - (-20) =$

13) $(-11) - 25 =$

14) $30 - (-16) =$

15) $56 - (45 - 23) =$

16) $15 - (-4) - (-34) =$

17) $(24 + 14) - (-55) =$

18) $23 - 15 - (-3) =$

19) $49 - (15 + 12) - (-4) =$

20) $29 - (-17) - (-25) =$

21) $12 - (-8) - (-18) =$

22) $(15 - 28) - (-22) =$

23) $19 - 44 - (-14) =$

24) $67 - (57 + 19) - (-8) =$

25) $56 - (-12) + (-19) =$

26) $22 - (-44) + (-55) =$

Multiplying and Dividing Integers

✍ *Find each product.*

1) $(-7) \times (-8) =$

2) $(-4) \times 5 =$

3) $5 \times (-11) =$

4) $(-5) \times (-20) =$

5) $-(2) \times (-8) \times 3 =$

6) $(12 - 4) \times (-10) =$

7) $14 \times (-10) \times (-5) =$

8) $(18 + 12) \times (-8) =$

9) $9 \times (-15 + 6) \times 3 =$

10) $(-5) \times (-8) \times (-12) =$

✍ *Find each quotient.*

11) $16 \div (-4) =$

12) $(-25) \div (-5) =$

13) $(-40) \div (-8) =$

14) $64 \div (-8) =$

15) $(-49) \div 7 =$

16) $(-112) \div (-4) =$

17) $168 \div (-12) =$

18) $(-121) \div (-11) =$

19) $216 \div (-12) =$

20) $-(152) \div (8) =$

21) $(-152) \div (-8) =$

22) $-216 \div (-12) =$

23) $(-198) \div (-9) =$

24) $195 \div (-13) =$

25) $-(182) \div (-7) =$

26) $(126) \div (-14) =$

Order of Operations

✎ **Evaluate each expression.**

1) $5 + (4 \times 2) =$

2) $13 - (2 \times 5) =$

3) $(16 \times 2) + 18 =$

4) $(12 - 5) - (4 \times 3) =$

5) $25 + (14 \div 2) =$

6) $(18 \times 5) \div 5 =$

7) $(48 \div 2) \times (-4) =$

8) $(7 \times 5) + (25 - 12) =$

9) $64 + (3 \times 2) + 8 =$

10) $(20 \times 5) \div (4 + 1) =$

11) $(-9) + (12 \times 6) + 15 =$

12) $(7 \times 8) - (56 \div 4) =$

13) $(4 \times 8 \div 2) - (17 + 11) =$

14) $(18 + 8 - 15) \times 5 - 3 =$

15) $(25 - 12 + 45) \times (95 \div 5) =$

16) $28 + \left(15 - (32 \div 2)\right) =$

17) $(6 + 7 - 4 - 9) + (18 \div 2) =$

18) $(95 - 17) + (10 - 25 + 9) =$

19) $(18 \times 2) + (15 \times 5) - 12 =$

20) $12 + 8 - (42 \times 4) + 50 =$

Integers and Absolute Value

✍ *Write absolute value of each number.*

1) $|-7| =$

2) $|-11| =$

3) $|-9| =$

4) $|8| =$

5) $|4| =$

6) $|-18| =$

7) $|6| =$

8) $|0| =$

9) $|16| =$

10) $|-2| =$

11) $|-12|$

12) $|10| =$

13) $|3| =$

14) $|7| =$

15) $|-15| =$

16) $|-13| =$

17) $|19| =$

18) $|-12| =$

19) $|4| =$

20) $|-25| =$

✍ *Evaluate the value.*

21) $|-2| - \frac{|-10|}{2} =$

22) $8 - |2 - 14| - |-2| =$

23) $\frac{|-36|}{6} \times |-6| =$

24) $\frac{|5 \times -3|}{5} \times \frac{|-20|}{4} =$

25) $|2 \times -4| + \frac{|-40|}{5} =$

26) $\frac{|-28|}{4} \times \frac{|-55|}{11} =$

27) $|-12 + 4| \times \frac{|-4 \times 5|}{2}$

28) $\frac{|-10 \times 3|}{2} \times |-12| =$

Answers – Chapter 3

Adding and Subtracting Integers

1) 7
2) −32
3) −20
4) 31
5) −14
6) 33
7) 16
8) 3
9) 5

10) 37
11) −4
12) 35
13) −36
14) 46
15) 34
16) 53
17) 93
18) 11

19) 26
20) 71
21) 38
22) 9
23) −11
24) −1
25) 49
26) 11

Multiplying and Dividing Integers

1) 56
2) −20
3) −55
4) 100
5) 48
6) −80
7) 700
8) −240
9) −243

10) −480
11) −4
12) 5
13) 5
14) −8
15) −7
16) 28
17) −14
18) 11

19) −18
20) −19
21) 19
22) 18
23) 22
24) −15
25) 26
26) −9

Order of Operations

1) 13
2) 3
3) 50
4) −5
5) 32
6) 18
7) −96

8) 48
9) 78
10) 20
11) 78
12) 42
13) −12
14) 52

15) 1,102
16) 27
17) 9
18) 72
19) 99
20) −98

Effortless
Math
Education

Integers and Absolute Value

1) 7
2) 11
3) 9
4) 8
5) 4
6) 18
7) 6
8) 0
9) 16
10) 2

11) 12
12) 10
13) 3
14) 7
15) 15
16) 13
17) 19
18) 12
19) 4
20) 25

21) -3
22) -6
23) 36
24) 15
25) 16
26) 35
27) 80
28) 180

Effortless Math Education

Chapter 4: Ratios and Proportions

Math Topics that you'll learn in this Chapter:

- ✓ Simplifying Ratios
- ✓ Proportional Ratios
- ✓ Create Proportion
- ✓ Similarity and Ratios
- ✓ Simple Interest

27

Simplifying Ratios

✎ Reduce each ratio.

1) $12:8 = $ ___:___

2) $2:20 = $ ___:___

3) $3:36 = $ ___:___

4) $8:16 = $ ___:___

5) $6:100 = $ ___:___

6) $10:60 = $ ___:___

7) $21:49 = $ ___:___

8) $20:40 = $ ___:___

9) $10:50 = $ ___:___

10) $14:18 = $ ___:___

11) $45:27 = $ ___:___

12) $49:21 = $ ___:___

13) $100:10 = $ ___:___

14) $35:45 = $ ___:___

15) $8:20 = $ ___:___

16) $25:35 = $ ___:___

17) $21:27 = $ ___:___

18) $52:82 = $ ___:___

19) $12:36 = $ ___:___

20) $24:3 = $ ___:___

21) $15:30 = $ ___:___

22) $14:63 = $ ___:___

23) $68:80 = $ ___:___

24) $8:80 = $ ___:___

✎ Write each ratio as a fraction in simplest form.

25) $2:4 = $

26) $6:20 = $

27) $5:35 = $

28) $10:55 = $

29) $8:24 = $

30) $9:42 = $

31) $12:48 = $

32) $6:40 = $

33) $15:36 = $

34) $18:82 = $

35) $22:26 = $

36) $8:36 = $

37) $16:128 = $

38) $14:77 = $

39) $12:180 = $

40) $36:108 = $

41) $24:42 = $

42) $18:120 = $

43) $44:82 = $

44) $60:240 = $

45) $36:180 = $

bit.ly/3nKwq0Z

Find more at

EffortlessMath.com

Proportional Ratios

✎ **Fill in the blanks; solve each proportion.**

1) $3 : 7$ = ___ $: 49$

2) $1 : 2$ = $20 :$ ___

3) $1 : 5$ = ___ $: 50$

4) $7 : 9$ = $14 :$ ___

5) $5 : 3$ = $45 :$ ___

6) $7 : 3$ = ___ $: 18$

7) $10 : 1$ = ___ $: 10$

8) $1 : 3$ = ___ $: 27$

9) $8 : 1$ = ___ $: 8$

10) $9 : 2$ = ___ $: 14$

11) $3 : 12$ = $12 :$ ___

12) $6 : 4$ = $24 :$ ___

✎ **State if each pair of ratios form a proportion.**

13) $\frac{3}{10}$ and $\frac{9}{30}$

14) $\frac{1}{2}$ and $\frac{16}{32}$

15) $\frac{5}{6}$ and $\frac{35}{42}$

16) $\frac{3}{7}$ and $\frac{27}{72}$

17) $\frac{2}{5}$ and $\frac{16}{45}$

18) $\frac{4}{9}$ and $\frac{40}{81}$

19) $\frac{6}{11}$ and $\frac{42}{77}$

20) $\frac{1}{6}$ and $\frac{8}{48}$

21) $\frac{6}{17}$ and $\frac{36}{85}$

22) $\frac{2}{7}$ and $\frac{24}{86}$

23) $\frac{12}{19}$ and $\frac{156}{247}$

24) $\frac{13}{21}$ and $\frac{182}{294}$

✎ **Solve each proportion.**

25) $\frac{2}{5} = \frac{14}{x}, x =$ ___

26) $\frac{1}{6} = \frac{7}{x}, x =$ ___

27) $\frac{3}{5} = \frac{27}{x}, x =$ ___

28) $\frac{1}{5} = \frac{x}{80}, x =$ ___

29) $\frac{3}{7} = \frac{x}{63}, x =$ ___

30) $\frac{1}{4} = \frac{13}{x}, x =$ ___

31) $\frac{7}{9} = \frac{56}{x}, x =$ ___

32) $\frac{6}{11} = \frac{42}{x}, x =$ ___

33) $\frac{4}{7} = \frac{x}{77}, x =$ ___

34) $\frac{5}{13} = \frac{x}{143}, x =$ ___

35) $\frac{7}{19} = \frac{x}{209}, x =$ ___

36) $\frac{3}{13} = \frac{x}{195}, x =$ ___

bit.ly/37GHQxp

Find more at

Create Proportion

✎ *State if each pair of ratios form a proportion.*

1) $\frac{3}{8}$ and $\frac{24}{50}$

2) $\frac{3}{11}$ and $\frac{6}{22}$

3) $\frac{4}{5}$ and $\frac{16}{20}$

4) $\frac{5}{11}$ and $\frac{12}{33}$

5) $\frac{5}{10}$ and $\frac{15}{30}$

6) $\frac{4}{13}$ and $\frac{8}{24}$

7) $\frac{6}{9}$ and $\frac{24}{36}$

8) $\frac{7}{12}$ and $\frac{14}{20}$

9) $\frac{3}{8}$ and $\frac{27}{72}$

10) $\frac{12}{20}$ and $\frac{36}{60}$

11) $\frac{11}{12}$ and $\frac{55}{60}$

12) $\frac{12}{15}$ and $\frac{24}{25}$

13) $\frac{15}{19}$ and $\frac{20}{38}$

14) $\frac{10}{14}$ and $\frac{40}{56}$

15) $\frac{11}{13}$ and $\frac{44}{39}$

16) $\frac{15}{16}$ and $\frac{30}{32}$

17) $\frac{17}{19}$ and $\frac{34}{48}$

18) $\frac{5}{18}$ and $\frac{15}{54}$

19) $\frac{3}{14}$ and $\frac{18}{42}$

20) $\frac{7}{11}$ and $\frac{14}{32}$

21) $\frac{8}{11}$ and $\frac{32}{44}$

22) $\frac{8}{14}$ and $\frac{24}{54}$

✎ *Solve.*

23) The ratio of boys to girls in a class is $3:4$. If there are 27 boys in the class, how many girls are in that class? _____

24) The ratio of red marbles to blue marbles in a bag is $5:6$. If there are 66 marbles in the bag, how many of the marbles are red? _____

25) You can buy 6 cans of green beans at a supermarket for $3.60. How much does it cost to buy 48 cans of green beans? _____

Similarity and Ratios

✎ *Each pair of figures is similar. Find the missing side.*

1)

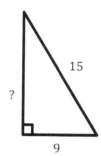

15
3
5
?
4
9

2)

9 9
3 3
6
?

3)

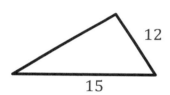

12
4
15
?

4)

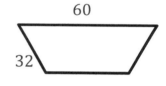

60
?
8
32

✎ *Solve.*

5) Two rectangles are similar. The first is 6 feet wide and 20 feet long. The second is 15 feet wide. What is the length of the second rectangle? _____

6) Two rectangles are similar. One is 2.5 meters by 9 meters. The longer side of the second rectangle is 22.5 meters. What is the other side of the second rectangle? _____

7) A building casts a shadow 24 ft long. At the same time a girl 5 ft tall casts a shadow 2 ft long. How tall is the building? _____

8) The scale of a map of Texas is 2 inches: 45 miles. If you measure the distance from Dallas to Martin County as 14.4 inches, approximately how far is Martin County from Dallas? _____

Simple Interest

✎ *Determine the simple interest for these loans.*

1) $450 at 7% for 2 years. $ _____

2) $5,200 at 4% for 3 years. $ _____

3) $1,300 at 5% for 6 years. $ _____

4) $5,400 at 3.5% for 6 months. $ _____

5) $600 at 4% for 9 months. $ _____

6) $24,000 at 5.5% for 5 years. $ _____

7) $15,600 at 3% for 2 years. $ _____

8) $1,200 at 5.5% for 4 years. $ _____

9) $1,600 at 4.5% for 9 months. $ _____

10) $12,000 at 2.2% for 5 years. $ _____

✎ *Solve each simple interest word problem.*

11) A new car, valued at $28,000, depreciates at 9% per year. What is the value of the car one year after purchase? $_____

12) Sara puts $4,000 into an investment yielding 5% annual simple interest; she left the money in for five years. How much interest does Sara get at the end of those five years? $_____

13) A bank is offering 3.5% simple interest on a savings account. If you deposit $7,500, how much interest will you earn in two years? $_____

14) $400 interest is earned on a principal of $2,000 at a simple interest rate of 5% interest per year. For how many years was the principal invested? _____

15) In how many years will $1,200 yield an interest of $180 at 3% simple interest? _____

16) Jim invested $4,000 in a bond at a yearly rate of 4.5%. He earned $540 in interest. How long was the money invested? _____

Answers – Chapter 4

Simplifying Ratios

1) 3 : 2
2) 1 : 10
3) 1 : 12
4) 1 : 2
5) 3 : 50
6) 1 : 6
7) 3 : 7
8) 1 : 2
9) 1 : 5
10) 7 : 9
11) 5 : 3
12) 7 : 3
13) 10 : 1
14) 7 : 9
15) 2 : 5
16) 5 : 7
17) 7 : 9
18) 26 : 41

19) 1 : 3
20) 8 : 1
21) 1 : 2
22) 2 : 9
23) 17 : 20
24) 1 : 10
25) $\frac{1}{2}$
26) $\frac{3}{10}$
27) $\frac{1}{7}$
28) $\frac{2}{11}$
29) $\frac{1}{3}$
30) $\frac{3}{14}$
31) $\frac{1}{4}$
32) $\frac{3}{20}$

33) $\frac{5}{12}$
34) $\frac{9}{41}$
35) $\frac{11}{13}$
36) $\frac{2}{9}$
37) $\frac{1}{8}$
38) $\frac{2}{11}$
39) $\frac{1}{15}$
40) $\frac{1}{3}$
41) $\frac{4}{7}$
42) $\frac{3}{20}$
43) $\frac{22}{41}$
44) $\frac{1}{4}$
45) $\frac{1}{5}$

Proportional Ratios

1) 21
2) 40
3) 10
4) 18
5) 27
6) 42
7) 100
8) 9
9) 64
10) 63
11) 48
12) 16

13) Yes
14) Yes
15) Yes
16) No
17) No
18) No
19) Yes
20) Yes
21) No
22) No
23) Yes
24) Yes

25) 35
26) 42
27) 45
28) 16
29) 27
30) 52
31) 72
32) 77
33) 44
34) 55
35) 77
36) 45

Effortless Math Education

Create Proportion

1) *No*
2) *Yes*
3) *Yes*
4) *No*
5) *Yes*
6) *No*
7) *Yes*
8) *No*
9) *Yes*
10) *Yes*
11) *Yes*
12) *No*
13) *No*
14) *Yes*
15) *No*
16) *Yes*
17) *No*
18) *Yes*
19) *No*
20) *No*
21) *Yes*
22) *No*
23) 36 *girls*
24) 30 *red marbles*
25) $28.80

Similarity and ratios

1) 12
2) 2
3) 5
4) 15
5) 50 feet
6) 6.25 meters
7) 60 feet
8) 324 miles

Simple Interest

1) $63.00
2) $624.00
3) $390.00
4) $94.50
5) $18.00
6) $6,600.00
7) $936.00
8) $264.00
9) $54.00
10) $1,320.00
11) $25,480.00
12) $1,000.00
13) $525.00
14) 4 years
15) 5 years
16) 3 years

Effortless Math Education

Chapter 5: Percentage

Math Topics that you'll learn in this Chapter:

- ✓ Percent Problems
- ✓ Percent of Increase and Decrease
- ✓ Discount, Tax and Tip

35

Percent Problems

✎ *Solve each problem.*

1) 20 is what percent of 50? ____%

2) 18 is what percent of 90? ____%

3) 12 is what percent of 15? ____%

4) 16 is what percent of 200? ____%

5) 24 is what percent of 800? ____%

6) 48 is what percent of 400? ____%

7) 90 is what percent of 750? ____%

8) 24 is what percent of 300? ____%

9) 60 is what percent of 400? ____%

10) 42 is what percent of 350? ___%

11) 11 is what percent of 44? ___%

12) 8 is what percent of 64? ___%

13) 210 is what percent of 875? ___%

14) 80 is what percent of 64? ___%

15) 15 is what percent of 12? ___%

16) 56 is what percent of 40? ___%

17) 36 is what percent of 240? ___%

18) 32 is what percent of 20? ___%

✎ *Solve each percent word problem.*

19) There are 48 employees in a company. On a certain day, 36 were present. What percent showed up for work? _____%

20) A metal bar weighs 24 ounces. 15% of the bar is gold. How many ounces of gold are in the bar? _____

21) A crew is made up of 12 women; the rest are men. If 20% of the crew are women, how many people are in the crew? _____

22) There are 48 students in a class and 6 of them are girls. What percent are boys? _____%

23) The Royals softball team played 75 games and won 60 of them. What percent of the games did they lose? _____%

Percent of Increase and Decrease

Find each percent of change.

1) From 200 to 500.   ___ %

2) From 50 ft to 75 ft.   ___ %

3) From $250 to $350.   ___ %

4) From 60 cm to 90 cm. ___ %

5) From 30 to 90.   ___ %

6) From 30 to 6.   ___ %

7) From 80 to 120.   ___ %

8) From 800 to 200.   ___ %

9) From 25 to 15.   ___ %

10) From 32 to 8.   ___ %

Solve each percent of change word problem.

11) Bob got a raise, and his hourly wage increased from $12 to $15. What is the percent increase? _____ %

12) The price of a pair of shoes increases from $20 to $32. What is the percent increase? ____ %

13) At a coffeeshop, the price of a cup of coffee increased from $1.20 to $1.44. What is the percent increase in the cost of the coffee? _____ %

14) 6 cm are cut from a 24 cm board. What is the percent decrease in length? _____ %

15) In a class, the number of students has been increased from 18 to 27. What is the percent increase? _____ %

16) The price of gasoline rose from $2.40 to $2.76 in one month. By what percent did the gas price rise? _____ %

17) A shirt was originally priced at $48. It went on sale for $38.40. What was the percent that the shirt was discounted? _____ %

bit.ly/3pgPQes

Find more at

Discount, Tax and Tip

✍️ *Find the selling price of each item.*

1) Original price of a computer: $500

    Tax: 6%   Selling price: $_____

2) Original price of a laptop: $350

    Tax: 8%   Selling price: $_____

3) Original price of a sofa: $800

    Tax: 7%   Selling price: $_____

4) Original price of a car: $18,500

    Tax: 8.5%   Selling price: $_____

5) Original price of a Table: $250

    Tax: 5%   Selling price: $_____

6) Original price of a house: $250,000

    Tax: 6.5%   Selling price: $_____

7) Original price of a tablet: $400

    Discount: 20%   Selling price: $_____

8) Original price of a chair: $150

    Discount: 15%   Selling price: $_____

9) Original price of a book: $50

    Discount: 25%   Selling price: $_____

10) Original price of a cellphone: $500

    Discount: 10%   Selling price: $_____

11) Food bill: $24

    Tip: 20%   Price: $_____

12) Food bill: $60

    Tipp: 15%   Price: $_____

13) Food bill: $32

    Tip: 20%   Price: $_____

14) Food bill: $18

    Tipp: 25%   Price: $_____

✍️ *Solve each word problem.*

15) Nicolas hired a moving company. The company charged $400 for its services, and Nicolas gives the movers a 15% tip. How much does Nicolas tip the movers? $_____

16) Mason has lunch at a restaurant and the cost of his meal is $30. Mason wants to leave a 20% tip. What is Mason's total bill including tip? $_____

17) The sales tax in Texas is 8.25% and an item costs $400. How much is the tax? $_____

18) The price of a table at Best Buy is $220. If the sales tax is 6%, what is the final price of the table including tax? $_____

Answers – Chapter 5

Percent Problems

1) 40%
2) 20%
3) 80%
4) 8%
5) 3%
6) 12%
7) 12%
8) 8%

9) 15%
10) 12%
11) 25%
12) 12.5%
13) 24%
14) 125%
15) 125%
16) 140%

17) 15%
18) 160%
19) 75%
20) 3.6 ounces
21) 60
22) 87.5%
23) 20%

Percent of Increase and Decrease

1) 150%
2) 50%
3) 40%
4) 50%
5) 200%
6) 80%

7) 50%
8) 75%
9) 40%
10) 75%
11) 25%
12) 60%

13) 20%
14) 25%
15) 50%
16) 15%
17) 20%

Discount, Tax and Tip

1) $530.00
2) $378.00
3) $856.00
4) $20,072.50
5) $262.50
6) $266,250

7) $320.00
8) $127.50
9) $37.50
10) $450.00
11) $28.80
12) $69.00

13) $38.40
14) $22.50
15) $60.00
16) $36.00
17) $33.00
18) $233.20

Effortless Math Education

Chapter 6: Expressions and Variables

Math Topics that you'll learn in this Chapter:

- ✓ Simplifying Variable Expressions
- ✓ Simplifying Polynomial Expressions
- ✓ Evaluating One Variable
- ✓ Evaluating Two Variables
- ✓ The Distributive Property

41

Simplifying Variable Expressions

✍ *Simplify each expression.*

1) $3(x + 9) =$

2) $(-6)(8x - 4) =$

3) $7x + 3 - 3x =$

4) $-2 - x^2 - 6x^2 =$

5) $3 + 10x^2 + 2 =$

6) $8x^2 + 6x + 7x^2 =$

7) $5x^2 - 12x^2 + 8x =$

8) $2x^2 - 2x - x =$

9) $4x + 6(2 - 5x) =$

10) $10x + 8(10x - 6) =$

11) $9(-2x - 6) - 5 =$

12) $2x^2 + (-8x) =$

13) $x - 3 + 5 - 3x =$

14) $2 - 3x + 12 - 2x =$

15) $32x - 4 + 23 + 2x =$

16) $(-6)(8x - 4) + 10x =$

17) $14x - 5(5 - 8x) =$

18) $23x + 4(9x + 3) + 12 =$

19) $3(-7x + 5) + 20x =$

20) $12x - 3x(x + 9) =$

21) $7x + 5x(3 - 3x) =$

22) $5x(-8x + 12) + 14x =$

23) $40x + 12 + 2x^2 =$

24) $5x(x - 3) - 10 =$

25) $8x - 7 + 8x + 2x^2 =$

26) $2x^2 - 5x - 7x =$

27) $7x - 3x^2 - 5x^2 - 3 =$

28) $4 + x^2 - 6x^2 - 12x =$

29) $12x + 8x^2 + 2x + 20 =$

30) $2x^2 + 6x + 3x^2 =$

31) $23 + 15x^2 + 8x - 4x^2 =$

32) $8x - 12x - x^2 + 13 =$

Simplifying Polynomial Expressions

✍ *Simplify each polynomial.*

1) $(2x^3 + 5x^2) - (12x + 2x^2) = $ _____

2) $(2x^5 + 2x^3) - (7x^3 + 6x^2) = $ _____

3) $(12x^4 + 4x^2) - (2x^2 - 6x^4) = $ _____

4) $14x - 3x^2 - 2(6x^2 + 6x^3) = $ _____

5) $(5x^3 - 3) + 5(2x^2 - 3x^3) = $ _____

6) $(4x^3 - 2x) - 2(4x^3 - 2x^4) = $ _____

7) $2(4x - 3x^3) - 3(3x^3 + 4x^2) = $ _____

8) $(2x^2 - 2x) - (2x^3 + 5x^2) = $ _____

9) $2x^3 - (4x^4 + 2x) + x^2 = $ _____

10) $x^4 - 2(x^2 + x) + 3x = $ _____

11) $(2x^2 - x^4) - (4x^4 - x^2) = $ _____

12) $4x^2 - 5x^3 + 15x^4 - 12x^3 = $ _____

13) $2x^2 - 5x^4 + 14x^4 - 11x^3 = $ _____

14) $2x^2 + 5x^3 - 7x^2 + 12x = $ _____

15) $2x^4 - 5x^5 + 8x^4 - 8x^2 = $ _____

16) $5x^3 + 15x - x^2 - 2x^3 = $ _____

Evaluating One Variable

✎ **Evaluate each expression using the value given.**

1) $5 + x$, $x = 2$

2) $x - 2, x = 4$

3) $8x + 1, x = 9$

4) $x - 12, x = -1$

5) $9 - x$, $x = 3$

6) $x + 2, x = 5$

7) $3x + 7, x = 6$

8) $x + (-5), x = -2$

9) $3x + 6, x = 4$

10) $4x + 6, x = -1$

11) $10 + 2x - 6, x = 3$

12) $10 - 3x, x = 8$

13) $2x - 5, x = 4$

14) $5x + 6, x = -3$

15) $12x + 6, x = 2$

16) $10 - 3x, x = -2$

17) $5(6x + 2), x = 8$

18) $2(-7x - 2), x = 3$

19) $9x - 3x + 12, x = 6$

20) $(6x + 3) \div 5, x = 2$

21) $(x + 16) \div 3, x = 8$

22) $4x - 12 + 8x, x = -6$

23) $(16 - 12x)(-2), x = -3$

24) $12x^2 + 5x - 3, x = 2$

25) $x^2 - 11x, x = -4$

26) $2x(6 - 4x), x = 5$

27) $14x + 7 - 3x^2, x = -3$

28) $(-5)(10x - 20 + 2x), x = 2$

29) $(-3) + \frac{x}{4} + 2x, x = 16$

30) $(-2) + \frac{x}{7}, x = 21$

31) $\left(-\frac{14}{x}\right) - 9 + 4x, x = 2$

32) $\left(-\frac{6}{x}\right) - 9 + 2x, x = 3$

Evaluating Two Variables

✍ *Evaluate each expression using the values given.*

1) $2x + 4y$,

  $x = 3, y = 2$

2) $8x + 5y$,

  $x = 1, y = 5$

3) $-2a + 4b$,

  $a = 6, b = 3$

4) $4x + 7 - 2y$,

  $x = 7, y = 6$

5) $5z + 12 - 4k$,

  $z = 5 , k = 2$

6) $2(-x - 2y)$,

  $x = 6, y = 9$

7) $18a + 2b$,

  $a = 2, b = 8$

8) $4x \div 3y$,

  $x = 3, y = 2$

9) $2x + 15 + 4y$,

  $x = -2, y = 4$

10) $4a - (15 - b)$,

  $a = 4, b = 6$

11) $5z + 19 + 8k$,

  $z = -5, k = 4$

12) $xy + 12 + 5x$,

  $x = 7, y = 2$

13) $2x + 4y - 3 + 2$,

  $x = 5, y = 3$

14) $\left(-\frac{12}{x}\right) + 1 + 5y$,

  $x = 6, y = 8$

15) $(-4)(-2a - 2b)$,

  $a = 5, b = 3$

16) $10 + 3x + 7 - 2y$,

  $x = 7, y = 6$

17) $9x + 2 - 4y + 5$,

  $x = 7, y = 5$

18) $6 + 3(-2x - 3y)$,

  $x = 9, y = 7$

19) $2x + 14 + 4y$,

  $x = 6, y = 8$

20) $4a - (5a - b) + 5$,

  $a = 4, b = 6$

The Distributive Property

 Use the distributive property to simply each expression.

1) $2(2 + 3x) =$

2) $3(5 + 5x) =$

3) $4(3x - 8) =$

4) $(6x - 2)(-2) =$

5) $(-3)(x + 2) =$

6) $(2 + 2x)5 =$

7) $(-4)(4 - 2x) =$

8) $-(-2 - 5x) =$

9) $(-6x + 2)(-1) =$

10) $(-5)(x - 2) =$

11) $-(7 - 3x) =$

12) $8(8 + 2x) =$

13) $2(12 + 2x) =$

14) $(-6x + 8)4 =$

15) $(3 - 6x)(-7) =$

16) $(-12)(2x + 1) =$

17) $(8 - 2x)9 =$

18) $5(7 + 9x) =$

19) $11(5x + 2) =$

20) $(-4x + 6)6 =$

21) $(3 - 6x)(-8) =$

22) $(-12)(2x - 3) =$

23) $(10 - 2x)9 =$

24) $(-5)(11x - 2) =$

25) $(1 - 9x)(-10) =$

26) $(-6)(x + 8) =$

27) $(-4 + 3x)(-8) =$

28) $(-5)(1 - 11x) =$

29) $11(3x - 12) =$

30) $(-12x + 14)(-5) =$

31) $(-5)(4x - 1) + 4(x + 2) =$

32) $(-3)(x + 4) - (2 + 3x) =$

Answers – Chapter 6

Simplifying Variable Expressions

1) $3x + 27$
2) $-48x + 24$
3) $4x + 3$
4) $-7x^2 - 2$
5) $10x^2 + 5$
6) $15x^2 + 6x$
7) $-7x^2 + 8x$
8) $2x^2 - 3x$
9) $-26x + 12$
10) $90x - 48$

11) $-18x - 59$
12) $2x^2 - 8x$
13) $-2x + 2$
14) $-5x + 14$
15) $34x + 19$
16) $-38x + 24$
17) $54x - 25$
18) $59x + 24$
19) $-x + 15$
20) $-3x^2 - 15x$
21) $-15x^2 + 22x$

22) $-40x^2 + 74x$
23) $2x^2 + 40x + 12$
24) $5x^2 - 15x - 10$
25) $2x^2 + 16x - 7$
26) $2x^2 - 12x$
27) $-8x^2 + 7x - 3$
28) $-5x^2 - 12x + 4$
29) $8x^2 + 14x + 20$
30) $5x^2 + 6x$
31) $11x^2 + 8x + 23$
32) $-x^2 - 4x + 13$

Simplifying Polynomial Expressions

1) $2x^3 + 3x^2 - 12x$
2) $2x^5 - 5x^3 - 6x^2$
3) $18x^4 + 2x^2$
4) $-12x^3 - 15x^2 + 14x$
5) $-10x^3 + 10x^2 - 3$
6) $4x^4 - 4x^3 - 2x$
7) $-15x^3 - 12x^2 + 8x$
8) $-2x^3 - 3x^2 - 2x$

9) $-4x^4 + 2x^3 + x^2 - 2x$
10) $x^4 - 2x^2 + x$
11) $-5x^4 + 3x^2$
12) $15x^4 - 17x^3 + 4x^2$
13) $9x^4 - 11x^3 + 2x^2$
14) $5x^3 - 5x^2 + 12x$
15) $-5x^5 + 10x^4 - 8x^2$
16) $3x^3 - x^2 + 15x$

Evaluating One Variables

1) 7
2) 2
3) 73
4) -13
5) 6
6) 7
7) 25
8) -7
9) 18
10) 2
11) 10

12) -14
13) 3
14) -9
15) 30
16) 16
17) 250
18) -46
19) 48
20) 3
21) 8
22) -84

23) -104
24) 55
25) 60
26) -140
27) -62
28) -20
29) 33
30) 1
31) -8
32) -5

Evaluating Two Variables

1) 14
2) 33

3) 0
4) 23

5) 29
6) -48

Effortless Math Education

7) 52
8) 2
9) 27
10) 7
11) 26
12) 61

13) 21
14) 39
15) 64
16) 26
17) 50

18) −111
19) 58
20) 7

The Distributive Property

1) $6x + 4$
2) $15x + 15$
3) $12x - 32$
4) $-12x + 4$
5) $-3x - 6$
6) $10x + 10$
7) $8x - 16$
8) $5x + 2$
9) $6x - 2$
10) $-5x + 10$
11) $3x - 7$

12) $16x + 64$
13) $4x + 24$
14) $-24x + 32$
15) $42x - 21$
16) $-24x - 12$
17) $-18x + 72$
18) $45x + 35$
19) $55x + 22$
20) $-24x + 36$
21) $48x - 24$
22) $-24x + 36$

23) $-18x + 90$
24) $-55x + 10$
25) $90x - 10$
26) $-6x - 48$
27) $-24x + 32$
28) $55x - 5$
29) $33x - 132$
30) $60x - 70$
31) $-16x + 13$
32) $-6x - 14$

Chapter 7: Equations and Inequalities

Math Topics that you'll learn in this Chapter:

- ✓ One–Step Equations
- ✓ Multi–Step Equations
- ✓ System of Equations
- ✓ Graphing Single–Variable Inequalities
- ✓ One–Step Inequalities
- ✓ Multi–Step Inequalities

49

One–Step Equations

🖎 *Solve each equation.*

1) $2x = 20, x = $ ____

2) $4x = 16, x = $ ____

3) $8x = 24, x = $ ____

4) $6x = 30, x = $ ____

5) $x + 5 = 8, x = $ ____

6) $x - 1 = 5, x = $ ____

7) $x - 8 = 3, x = $ ____

8) $x + 6 = 12, x = $ ____

9) $x - 2 = 17, x = $ ____

10) $8 = 12 + x, x = $ ____

11) $x - 5 = 4, x = $ ____

12) $2 - x = -12, x = $ ____

13) $16 = -4 + x, x = $ ____

14) $x - 4 = -25, x = $ ____

15) $x + 12 = -9, x = $ ____

16) $14 = 18 - x, x = $ ____

17) $2 + x = -14, x = $ ____

18) $x - 5 = 15, x = $ ____

19) $25 = x - 5, x = $ ____

20) $x - 3 = -12, x = $ ____

21) $x - 12 = 12, x = $ ____

22) $x - 12 = -25, x = $ ____

23) $x - 13 = 32, x = $ ____

24) $-55 = x - 18, x = $ ____

25) $x - 12 = 18, x = $ ____

26) $20 = 5x, x = $ ____

27) $x - 30 = 20, x = $ ____

28) $x - 12 = 32, x = $ ____

29) $36 - x = 3, x = $ ____

30) $x - 14 = 14, x = $ ____

31) $19 - x = -15, x = $ ____

32) $x - 19 = -35, x = $ ____

Multi-Step Equations

✎ *Solve each equation.*

1) $2x + 3 = 5$

2) $-x + 8 = 5$

3) $3x - 4 = 5$

4) $-(2 - x) = 5$

5) $2x - 18 = 12$

6) $4x - 2 = 6$

7) $2x - 14 = 4$

8) $5x + 10 = 25$

9) $8x + 9 = 25$

10) $-3(2 + x) = 3$

11) $-2(4 + x) = 4$

12) $20 = -(x - 8)$

13) $2(2 - 2x) = 20$

14) $-12 = -(2x + 8)$

15) $5(2 + x) = 5$

16) $2(x - 14) = 4$

17) $-28 = 2x + 12x$

18) $3x + 15 = -x - 5$

19) $2(3 + 2x) = -18$

20) $12 - 2x = -8 - x$

21) $10 - 3x = 14 + x$

22) $10 + 10x = -2 + 4x$

23) $24 = (-4x) - 8 + 8$

24) $12 = 2x - 12 + 6x$

25) $-12 = -4x - 6 + 2x$

26) $4x - 12 = -18 + 5x$

27) $5x - 10 = 2x + 5$

28) $-7 - 3x = 2(3 - 2x)$

29) $x - 2 = -3(6 - 3x)$

30) $10x - 56 = 12x - 114$

31) $4x - 8 = -4(11 + 2x)$

32) $-5x - 14 = 6x + 52$

Systems of Equations

✎ **Solve each system of equations.**

1) $-2x + 2y = 4$ $x =$ ____
     $-2x + y = 3$ $y =$ ____

2) $-10x + 2y = -6$ $x =$ ____
     $6x - 16y = 48$ $y =$ ____

3) $y = -8$ $x =$ ____
     $16x - 12y = 32$

4) $2y = -6x + 10$ $x =$ ____
     $10x - 8y = -6$ $y =$ ____

5) $10x - 9y = -13$ $x =$ ____
     $-5x + 3y = 11$ $y =$ ____

6) $-3x - 4y = 5$ $x =$ ____
     $x - 2y = 5$ $y =$ ____

7) $5x - 14y = -23$ $x =$ ____
     $-6x + 7y = 8$ $y =$ ____

8) $10x - 14y = -4$ $x =$ ____
     $-10x - 20y = -30$ $y =$ ____

9) $-4x + 12y = 12$ $x =$ ____
     $-14x + 16y = -10$ $y =$ ____

10) $x + 20y = 56$ $x =$ ____
     $x + 15y = 41$ $y =$ ____

11) $6x - 7y = -8$ $x =$ ____
     $-x - 4y = -9$ $y =$ ____

12) $-3x + 2y = -18$ $x =$ ____
     $8x - 2y = 28$ $y =$ ____

13) $-5x + y = -3$ $x =$ ____
     $3x - 8y = 24$ $y =$ ____

14) $3x - 2y = 2$ $x =$ ____
     $5x - 5y = 10$ $y =$ ____

15) $8x + 14y = 4$ $x =$ ____
     $-6x - 7y = -10$ $y =$ ____

16) $10x + 7y = 1$ $x =$ ____
     $-5x - 7y = 24$ $y =$ ____

Graphing Single–Variable Inequalities

✎ *Draw a graph for each inequality.*

1) $x > 2$

2) $x < 5$

3) $x > -1$

4) $x < 3$

5) $x < -5$

6) $x > -2$

7) $x < 0$

8) $x > 4$

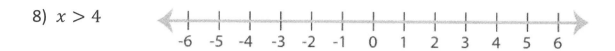

One–Step Inequalities

✍ *Solve each inequality and graph it.*

1) $x + 2 \geq 3$

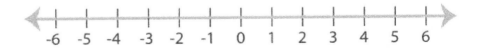

2) $x - 1 \leq 2$

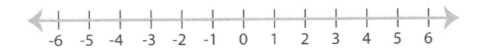

3) $2x \geq 12$

4) $4 + x \leq 5$

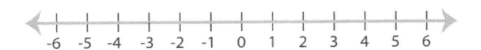

5) $x + 3 \leq -3$

6) $4x \geq 16$

7) $9x \leq 18$

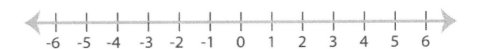

8) $x + 2 \geq 7$

Multi-Step Inequalities

✏️ **Solve each inequality.**

1) $x - 2 \leq 6$

2) $3 - x \leq 3$

3) $2x - 4 \leq 8$

4) $3x - 5 \geq 16$

5) $x - 5 \geq 10$

6) $2x - 8 \leq 6$

7) $8x - 2 \leq 14$

8) $-5 + 3x \leq 10$

9) $2(x - 3) \leq 6$

10) $7x - 5 \leq 9$

11) $4x - 21 < 19$

12) $2x - 3 < 21$

13) $17 - 3x \geq -13$

14) $9 + 4x < 21$

15) $3 + 2x \geq 19$

16) $6 + 2x < 32$

17) $4x - 1 < 7$

18) $3(3 - 2x) \geq -15$

19) $-(3 + 4x) < 13$

20) $20 - 8x \geq -28$

21) $-3(x - 7) > 21$

22) $\frac{2x+6}{4} \leq 10$

23) $\frac{4x+8}{2} \leq 12$

24) $\frac{3x-8}{7} > 1$

25) $4 + \frac{x}{3} < 7$

26) $\frac{9x}{7} - 7 < 2$

27) $\frac{4x+12}{4} > 1$

28) $15 + \frac{x}{5} < 12$

Answers – Chapter 7

One–Step Equations

1) 10
2) 4
3) 3
4) 5
5) 3
6) 6
7) 11
8) 6
9) 19
10) −4
11) 9

12) 14
13) 20
14) −21
15) −21
16) 4
17) −16
18) 20
19) 30
20) −9
21) 24
22) −13

23) 45
24) −37
25) 30
26) 4
27) 50
28) 44
29) 33
30) 28
31) 34
32) −16

Multi–Step Equations

1) 1
2) 3
3) 3
4) 7
5) 15
6) 2
7) 9
8) 3
9) 2
10) −3
11) −6

12) −12
13) −4
14) 2
15) −1
16) 16
17) −2
18) −5
19) −6
20) 20
21) −1
22) −2

23) −6
24) 3
25) 3
26) 6
27) 5
28) 13
29) 2
30) 29
31) −3
32) −6

Systems of Equations

1) $x = -1, y = 1$
2) $x = 0, y = -3$
3) $x = -4$
4) $x = 1, y = 2$
5) $x = -4, y = -3$
6) $x = 1, y = -2$

7) $x = 1, y = 2$
8) $x = 1, y = 1$
9) $x = 3, y = 2$
10) $x = -4, y = 3$
11) $x = 1, y = 2$
12) $x = 2, y = -6$

13) $x = 0, y = -3$
14) $x = -2, y = -4$
15) $x = 4, y = -2$
16) $x = 5, y = -7$

Effortless
Math
Education

Graphing Single-Variable Inequalities

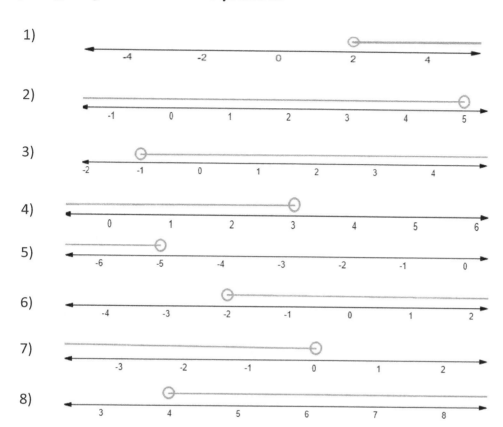

1)

2)

3)

4)

5)

6)

7)

8)

One-Step Inequalities

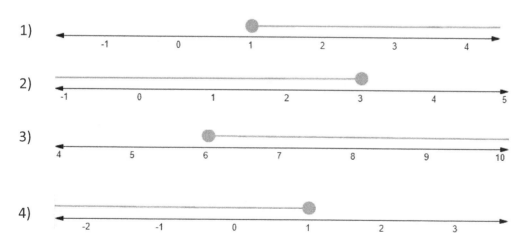

1)

2)

3)

4)

Effortless Math Education

5)

6)

7)

8)

Multi-Step Inequalities

1) $x \leq 8$
2) $x \geq 0$
3) $x \leq 6$
4) $x \geq 7$
5) $x \geq 15$
6) $x \leq 7$
7) $x \leq 2$
8) $x \leq 5$
9) $x \leq 6$
10) $x \leq 2$

11) $x < 10$
12) $x < 12$
13) $x \leq 10$
14) $x < 3$
15) $x \geq 8$
16) $x < 13$
17) $x < 2$
18) $x \leq 4$
19) $x > -4$
20) $x \leq 6$

21) $x < 0$
22) $x \leq 17$
23) $x \leq 4$
24) $x > 5$
25) $x < 9$
26) $x < 7$
27) $x > -2$
28) $x < -15$

Chapter 8: Exponents and Variables

Math Topics that you'll learn in this Chapter:

- ✓ Multiplication Property of Exponents
- ✓ Division Property of Exponents
- ✓ Powers of Products and Quotients
- ✓ Zero and Negative Exponents
- ✓ Negative Exponents and Negative Bases
- ✓ Scientific Notation
- ✓ Radicals

59

Multiplication Property of Exponents

✍️ *Simplify and write the answer in exponential form.*

1) $2 \times 2^2 =$

2) $5^3 \times 5 =$

3) $3^2 \times 3^2 =$

4) $4^2 \times 4^2 =$

5) $7^3 \times 7^2 \times 7 =$

6) $2 \times 2^2 \times 2^2 =$

7) $5^3 \times 5^2 \times 5 \times 5 =$

8) $2x \times x =$

9) $x^3 \times x^2 =$

10) $x^4 \times x^4 =$

11) $x^2 \times x^2 \times x^2 =$

12) $6x \times 6x =$

13) $2x^2 \times 2x^2 =$

14) $3x^2 \times x =$

15) $4x^4 \times 4x^4 \times 4x^4 =$

16) $2x^2 \times x^2 =$

17) $x^4 \times 3x =$

18) $x \times 2x^2 =$

19) $5x^4 \times 5x^4 =$

20) $2yx^2 \times 2x =$

21) $3x^4 \times y^2x^4 =$

22) $y^2x^3 \times y^5x^2 =$

23) $4yx^3 \times 2x^2y^3 =$

24) $6x^2 \times 6x^3y^4 =$

25) $3x^4y^5 \times 7x^2y^3 =$

26) $7x^2y^5 \times 9xy^3 =$

27) $7xy^4 \times 4x^3y^3 =$

28) $3x^5y^3 \times 8x^2y^3 =$

29) $3x \times y^5x^3 \times y^4 =$

30) $yx^2 \times 2y^2x^2 \times 2xy =$

31) $4yx^4 \times 5y^5x \times xy^3 =$

32) $7x^3 \times 10y^3x^5 \times 8yx^3 =$

Division Property of Exponents

 Simplify.

1) $\dfrac{2^2}{2^3} =$

2) $\dfrac{2^4}{2^2} =$

3) $\dfrac{5^5}{5} =$

4) $\dfrac{3}{3^5} =$

5) $\dfrac{x}{x^3} =$

6) $\dfrac{3 \times 3^3}{3^2 \times 3^4} =$

7) $\dfrac{5^8}{5^3} =$

8) $\dfrac{5 \times 5^6}{5^2 \times 5^7} =$

9) $\dfrac{3^4 \times 3^7}{3^2 \times 3^8} =$

10) $\dfrac{5x}{10x^3} =$

11) $\dfrac{3x^3}{2x^5} =$

12) $\dfrac{12x^3}{14x^6} =$

13) $\dfrac{12x^3}{9y^8} =$

14) $\dfrac{25xy^4}{5x^6y^2} =$

15) $\dfrac{2x^4}{7x} =$

16) $\dfrac{16x^2y^8}{4x^3} =$

17) $\dfrac{12x^4}{15x^7y^9} =$

18) $\dfrac{12yx^4}{10yx^8} =$

19) $\dfrac{16x^4y}{9x^8y^2} =$

20) $\dfrac{5x^8}{20x^8} =$

21) $\dfrac{2x^{-5}}{9x^{-2}} =$

Powers of Products and Quotients

✐ **Simplify.**

1) $(4^2)^2 =$

2) $(6^2)^3 =$

3) $(2 \times 2^3)^4 =$

4) $(4 \times 4^4)^2 =$

5) $(3^3 \times 3^2)^3 =$

6) $(5^4 \times 5^5)^2 =$

7) $(2 \times 2^4)^2 =$

8) $(2^6)^2 =$

9) $(11x^5)^2 =$

10) $(4x^2y^4)^4 =$

11) $(2x^4y^4)^3 =$

12) $(3x^2y^2)^2 =$

13) $(3x^4y^3)^4 =$

14) $(2x^6y^8)^2 =$

15) $(12x^3x)^3 =$

16) $(2x^9x^6)^3 =$

17) $(5x^{10}y^3)^3 =$

18) $(4x^3x^3)^2 =$

19) $(3x^3 . 5x)^2 =$

20) $(10x^{11}y^3)^2 =$

21) $(9x^7y^5)^2 =$

22) $(4x^4y^6)^5 =$

23) $(3x . 4y^3)^2 =$

24) $\left(\frac{5x}{x^2}\right)^2 =$

25) $\left(\frac{x^4y^4}{x^2y^2}\right)^3 =$

26) $\left(\frac{25x}{5x^6}\right)^2 =$

27) $\left(\frac{x^8}{x^6y^2}\right)^2 =$

28) $\left(\frac{xy^2}{x^3y^3}\right)^{-2} =$

29) $\left(\frac{2xy^4}{x^3}\right)^2 =$

30) $\left(\frac{xy^4}{5xy^2}\right)^{-3} =$

Zero and Negative Exponents

✎ *Evaluate the following expressions.*

1) $1^{-1} =$

2) $2^{-2} =$

3) $0^{15} =$

4) $1^{-10} =$

5) $8^{-1} =$

6) $8^{-2} =$

7) $2^{-4} =$

8) $10^{-2} =$

9) $9^{-1} =$

10) $3^{-2} =$

11) $7^{-2} =$

12) $3^{-4} =$

13) $6^{-2} =$

14) $5^{-3} =$

15) $22^{-1} =$

16) $4^{-2} =$

17) $5^{-2} =$

18) $35^{-1} =$

19) $4^{-3} =$

20) $6^{-3} =$

21) $3^{-5} =$

22) $5^{-4} =$

23) $2^{-3} =$

24) $3^{-3} =$

25) $7^{-3} =$

26) $6^{-4} =$

27) $8^{-3} =$

28) $9^{-2} =$

29) $10^{-3} =$

30) $10^{-9} =$

31) $\left(\frac{1}{2}\right)^{-1}$

32) $\left(\frac{1}{2}\right)^{-2} =$

33) $\left(\frac{1}{3}\right)^{-2} =$

34) $\left(\frac{2}{3}\right)^{-2} =$

35) $\left(\frac{1}{5}\right)^{-3} =$

36) $\left(\frac{3}{4}\right)^{-2} =$

37) $\left(\frac{2}{5}\right)^{-2} =$

38) $\left(\frac{1}{2}\right)^{-8} =$

39) $\left(\frac{2}{5}\right)^{-3} =$

40) $\left(\frac{3}{7}\right)^{-2} =$

41) $\left(\frac{5}{6}\right)^{-3} =$

42) $\left(\frac{4}{9}\right)^{-2} =$

Negative Exponents and Negative Bases

✎ **Simplify.**

1) $-6^{-1} =$

2) $-5^{-2} =$

3) $-2^{-4} =$

4) $-x^{-3} =$

5) $2x^{-1} =$

6) $-4x^{-3} =$

7) $-12x^{-5} =$

8) $-5x^{-2}y^{-3} =$

9) $20x^{-4}y^{-1} =$

10) $14a^{-6}b^{-7} =$

11) $-12x^2y^{-3} =$

12) $-\dfrac{25}{x^{-6}} =$

13) $-\dfrac{2x}{a^{-4}} =$

14) $\left(-\dfrac{1}{3}\right)^{-2} =$

15) $\left(-\dfrac{3}{4}\right)^{-2} =$

16) $-\dfrac{9}{a^{-7}b^{-2}} =$

17) $-\dfrac{5x}{x^{-3}} =$

18) $-\dfrac{a^{-3}}{b^{-2}} =$

19) $-\dfrac{5}{x^{-3}} =$

20) $\dfrac{7b}{-9c^{-4}} =$

21) $\dfrac{7ab}{a^{-3}b^{-1}} =$

22) $-\dfrac{5n^{-2}}{10p^{-3}} =$

23) $\dfrac{4ab^{-2}}{-3c^{-2}} =$

24) $\left(\dfrac{3a}{2c}\right)^{-2} =$

25) $\left(-\dfrac{5x}{3yz}\right)^{-3} =$

26) $\dfrac{4b^{-2}}{2c^3} =$

27) $\left(-\dfrac{x^3}{x^4}\right)^{-2} =$

28) $\left(-\dfrac{x^{-2}}{3x^2}\right)^{-3} =$

29) $\left(-\dfrac{x^{-4}}{x^2}\right)^{-2} =$

Scientific Notation

✎ **Write each number in scientific notation.**

1) 0.113 =

2) 0.02 =

3) 2.5 =

4) 20 =

5) 60 =

6) 0.004 =

7) 78 =

8) 1,600 =

9) 1,450 =

10) 91,000 =

11) 2,000,000 =

12) 0.0000006 =

13) 354,000 =

14) 0.000325 =

15) 0.00023 =

16) 56,000,000 =

17) 21,000 =

18) 78,000,000 =

19) 0.0000022 =

20) 0.00012 =

✎ **Write each number in standard notation.**

21) 3×10^{-1} =

22) 5×10^{-2} =

23) 1.2×10^{3} =

24) 2×10^{-4} =

25) 1.5×10^{-2} =

26) 4×10^{3} =

27) 9×10^{5} =

28) 1.12×10^{4} =

29) 3×10^{-5} =

30) 8.3×10^{-5} =

Radicals

✏ *Simplify and write the answer.*

1) $\sqrt{0} =$ ____

2) $\sqrt{1} =$ ____

3) $\sqrt{4} =$ ____

4) $\sqrt{16} =$ ____

5) $\sqrt{9} =$ ____

6) $\sqrt{25} =$ ____

7) $\sqrt{49} =$ ____

8) $\sqrt{36} =$ ____

9) $\sqrt{64} =$ ____

10) $\sqrt{81} =$ ____

11) $\sqrt{121} =$ ____

12) $\sqrt{225} =$ ____

13) $\sqrt{144} =$ ____

14) $\sqrt{100} =$ ____

15) $\sqrt{256} =$ ____

16) $\sqrt{289} =$ ____

17) $\sqrt{324} =$ ____

18) $\sqrt{400} =$ ____

19) $\sqrt{900} =$ ____

20) $\sqrt{529} =$ ____

21) $\sqrt{90} =$ ____

22) $\sqrt{169} =$ ____

23) $\sqrt{196} =$ ____

24) $\sqrt{361} =$ ____

✏ *Evaluate.*

25) $\sqrt{4} \times \sqrt{16} =$ _____

26) $\sqrt{25} \times \sqrt{64} =$ _____

27) $\sqrt{2} \times \sqrt{8} =$ _____

28) $\sqrt{6} \times \sqrt{6} =$ _____

29) $\sqrt{5} \times \sqrt{5} =$ _____

30) $\sqrt{8} \times \sqrt{8} =$ _____

31) $\sqrt{2} + \sqrt{2} =$ _____

32) $\sqrt{8} + \sqrt{8} =$ _____

33) $4\sqrt{5} - 2\sqrt{5} =$ _____

34) $3\sqrt{3} \times 2\sqrt{3} =$ _____

35) $8\sqrt{2} \times 2\sqrt{2} =$ _____

36) $6\sqrt{3} - \sqrt{12} =$ _____

Answers – Chapter 8

Multiplication Property of Exponents

1) 2^3
2) 5^4
3) 3^4
4) 4^4
5) 7^6
6) 2^5
7) 5^7
8) $2x^2$
9) x^5
10) x^8
11) x^6

12) $36x^2$
13) $4x^4$
14) $3x^3$
15) $64x^{12}$
16) $2x^4$
17) $3x^5$
18) $2x^3$
19) $25x^8$
20) $4x^3y$
21) $3x^8y^2$
22) x^5y^7

23) $8x^5y^4$
24) $36x^5y^4$
25) $21x^6y^8$
26) $63x^3y^8$
27) $28x^4y^7$
28) $24x^7y^6$
29) $3x^4y^9$
30) $4x^5y^4$
31) $20x^6y^9$
32) $560x^{11}y^4$

Division Property of Exponents

1) $\frac{1}{2}$
2) 2^2
3) 5^4
4) $\frac{1}{3^4}$
5) $\frac{1}{x^2}$
6) $\frac{1}{3^2}$
7) 5^5
8) $\frac{1}{25}$

9) 3
10) $\frac{1}{2x^2}$
11) $\frac{3}{2x^2}$
12) $\frac{6}{7x^3}$
13) $\frac{4x^3}{3y^8}$
14) $\frac{5y^2}{x^5}$
15) $\frac{2x^3}{7}$

16) $\frac{4y^8}{x}$
17) $\frac{4}{5x^3y^9}$
18) $\frac{6}{5x^4}$
19) $\frac{16}{9x^4y}$
20) $\frac{1}{4}$
21) $\frac{2}{9x^3}$

Powers of Products and Quotients

1) 4^4
2) 6^6
3) 2^{16}
4) 4^{10}
5) 3^{15}
6) 5^{18}
7) 2^{10}
8) 2^{12}

9) $121x^{10}$
10) $256x^8y^{16}$
11) $8x^{12}y^{12}$
12) $9x^4y^4$
13) $81x^{16}y^{12}$
14) $4x^{12}y^{16}$
15) $1,728x^{12}$
16) $8x^{45}$

17) $125x^{30}y^9$
18) $16x^{12}$
19) $225x^8$
20) $100x^{22}y^6$
21) $81x^{14}y^{10}$
22) $1,024x^{20}y^{30}$

Effortless
Math
Education

23) $144x^2y^6$

24) $\frac{25}{x^2}$

25) x^6y^6

26) $\frac{25}{x^{10}}$

27) $\frac{x^4}{y^4}$

28) x^4y^2

29) $\frac{4y^8}{x^4}$

30) $\frac{125}{y^6}$

Zero and Negative Exponents

1) 1

2) $\frac{1}{4}$

3) 0

4) 1

5) $\frac{1}{8}$

6) $\frac{1}{64}$

7) $\frac{1}{16}$

8) $\frac{1}{100}$

9) $\frac{1}{9}$

10) $\frac{1}{9}$

11) $\frac{1}{49}$

12) $\frac{1}{81}$

13) $\frac{1}{36}$

14) $\frac{1}{125}$

15) $\frac{1}{22}$

16) $\frac{1}{16}$

17) $\frac{1}{25}$

18) $\frac{1}{35}$

19) $\frac{1}{64}$

20) $\frac{1}{216}$

21) $\frac{1}{243}$

22) $\frac{1}{625}$

23) $\frac{1}{8}$

24) $\frac{1}{27}$

25) $\frac{1}{343}$

26) $\frac{1}{1,296}$

27) $\frac{1}{512}$

28) $\frac{1}{81}$

29) $\frac{1}{1,000}$

30) $\frac{1}{1,000,000,000}$

31) 2

32) 4

33) 9

34) $\frac{9}{4}$

35) 125

36) $\frac{16}{9}$

37) $\frac{25}{4}$

38) 256

39) $\frac{125}{8}$

40) $\frac{49}{9}$

41) $\frac{216}{125}$

42) $\frac{81}{16}$

Negative Exponents and Negative Bases

1) $-\frac{1}{6}$

2) $-\frac{1}{25}$

3) $-\frac{1}{16}$

4) $-\frac{1}{x^3}$

5) $\frac{2}{x}$

6) $-\frac{4}{x^3}$

7) $-\frac{12}{x^5}$

8) $-\frac{5}{x^2y^3}$

9) $\frac{20}{x^4y}$

10) $\frac{14}{a^6b^7}$

11) $-\frac{12x^2}{y^3}$

12) $-25x^6$

13) $-2xa^4$

14) 9

15) $\frac{16}{9}$

16) $-9a^7b^2$

17) $-5x^4$

18) $-\frac{b^2}{a^3}$

19) $-5x^3$

20) $-\frac{7bc^4}{9}$

21) $7a^4b^2$

22) $-\frac{p^3}{2n^2}$

23) $-\frac{4ac^2}{3b^2}$

24) $\frac{4c^2}{9a^2}$

25) $-\frac{27y^3z^3}{125x^3}$

26) $\frac{2}{b^2c^3}$

27) x^2

28) $-27x^{12}$

29) x^{12}

Scientific Notation

1) 1.13×10^{-1}

2) 2×10^{-2}

3) 2.5×10^0

4) 2×10^1

5) 6×10^1

6) 4×10^{-3}

7) 7.8×10^1

8) 1.6×10^3

9) 1.45×10^3

10) 9.1×10^4

11) 2×10^6

12) 6×10^{-7}

13) 3.54×10^5

14) 3.25×10^{-4}

15) 2.3×10^{-4}

16) 5.6×10^7

17) 2.1×10^4

18) 7.8×10^7

19) 2.2×10^{-6}

20) 1.2×10^{-4}

21) 0.3

22) 0.05

23) $1,200$

24) 0.0002

25) 0.015

26) $4,000$

27) $900,000$

28) $11,200$

29) 0.00003

30) 0.000083

Radicals

1) 0

2) 1

3) 2

4) 4

5) 3

6) 5

7) 7

8) 6

9) 8

10) 9

11) 11

12) 15

13) 12

14) 10

15) 16

16) 17

17) 18

18) 20

19) 30

20) 23

21) $3\sqrt{10}$

22) 13

23) 14

24) 19

25) 8

26) 40

27) 4

28) 6

29) 5

30) 8

31) $2\sqrt{2}$

32) $2\sqrt{8}$

33) $2\sqrt{5}$

34) 18

35) 32

36) $4\sqrt{3}$

Effortless
Math
Education

Chapter 9: Geometry and Solid Figures

Math Topics that you'll learn in this Chapter:

- ✓ The Pythagorean Theorem
- ✓ Triangles
- ✓ Polygons
- ✓ Circles
- ✓ Trapezoids
- ✓ Cubes
- ✓ Rectangle Prisms
- ✓ Cylinder

Pythagorean Theorem

 Do the following lengths form a right triangle?

1)	2)	3)	4)
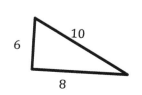	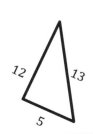	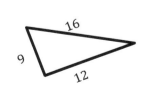	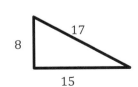

5)	6)	7)	8)
	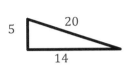	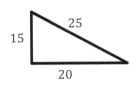	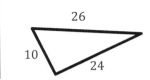

 Find the missing side.

9)	10)	11)	12)
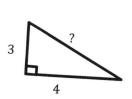	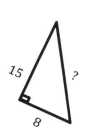	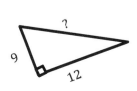	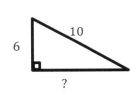

13)	14)	15)	16)
		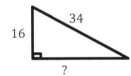	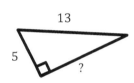

Triangles

✏️ *Find the measure of the unknown angle in each triangle.*

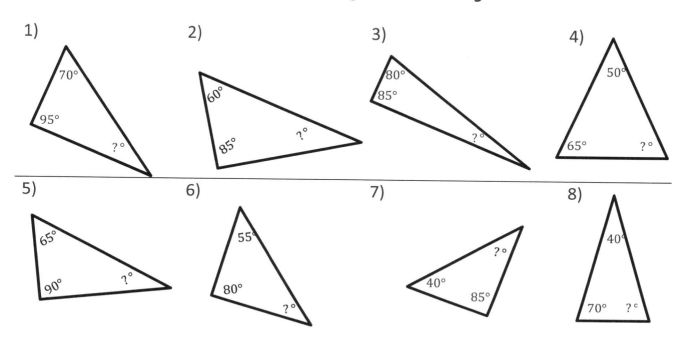

1) 70° 95° ?°

2) 60° 85° ?°

3) 80° 85° ?°

4) 50° 65° ?°

5) 65° 90° ?°

6) 55° 80° ?°

7) 40° 85° ?°

8) 40° 70° ?°

✏️ *Find area of each triangle.*

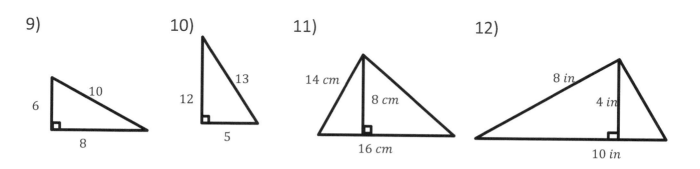

9) 6 10 8

10) 12 13 5

11) 14 cm 8 cm 16 cm

12) 8 in 4 in 10 in

Polygons

✏️ *Find the perimeter of each shape.*

1)

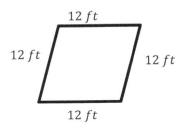

2)

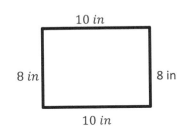

3)

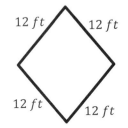

4) Square

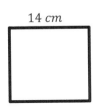

5) Regular hexagon

6)

7) Parallelogram

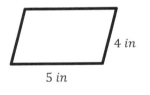

8) Square

✏️ *Find the area of each shape.*

9) Parallelogram

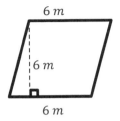

10) Rectangle

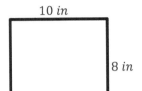

11) Rectangle

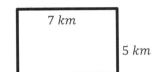

12) Square

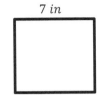

Circles

✏️ **Find the Circumference of each circle.** (π = 3.14)

1) ____   2) ____   3) ____   4) ____   5) ____   6) ____

7) ____   8) ____   9) ____   10) ____   11) ____   12) ____

✏️ **Complete the table below.** (π = 3.14)

	Radius	Diameter	Circumference	Area
Circle 1	2 inches	4 inches	12.56 inches	12.56 square inches
Circle 2		8 meters		
Circle 3				113.04 square ft
Circle 4			50.24 miles	
Circle 5		9 km		
Circle 6	7 cm			
Circle 7		10 feet		
Circle 8				615.44 square meters
Circle 9			81.64 inches	
Circle 10	12 feet			

Trapezoids

✎ *Find the area of each trapezoid.*

1)

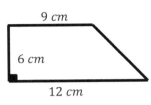

2)

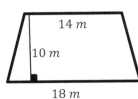

3)

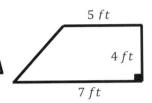

4)

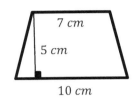

5)

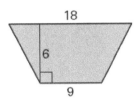

6)

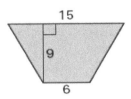

7)

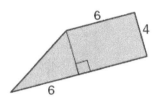

8)

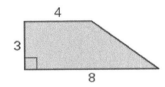

✎ *Solve.*

9) A trapezoid has an area of $60\ cm^2$ and its height is $6\ cm$ and one base is $8\ cm$. What is the other base length? _____

10) If a trapezoid has an area of $65\ ft^2$ and the lengths of the bases are $12\ ft$ and $14\ ft$, find the height. _____

11) If a trapezoid has an area of $180\ m^2$ and its height is $12\ m$ and one base is $20\ m$, find the other base length. _____

12) The area of a trapezoid is $625\ ft^2$ and its height is $25\ ft$. If one base of the trapezoid is $15\ ft$, what is the other base length? _____

Cubes

✎ **Find the volume of each cube.**

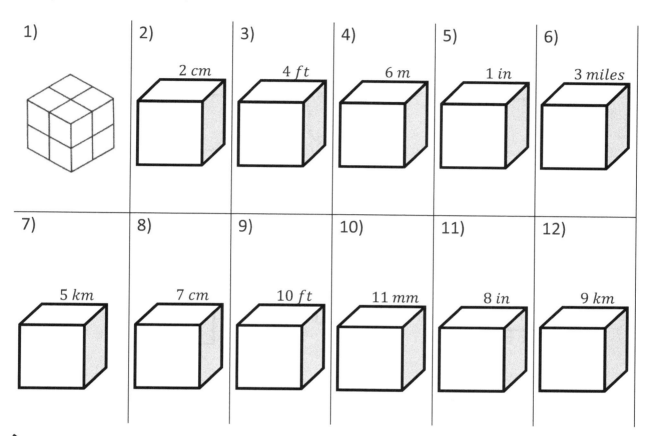

1)

2) 2 cm

3) 4 ft

4) 6 m

5) 1 in

6) 3 miles

7) 5 km

8) 7 cm

9) 10 ft

10) 11 mm

11) 8 in

12) 9 km

✎ **Find the surface area of each cube.**

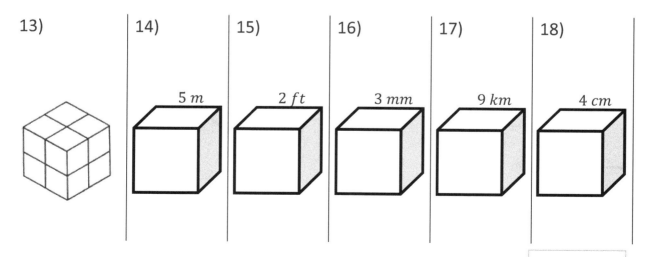

13)

14) 5 m

15) 2 ft

16) 3 mm

17) 9 km

18) 4 cm

Rectangular Prism

✍ *Find the volume of each Rectangular Prism.*

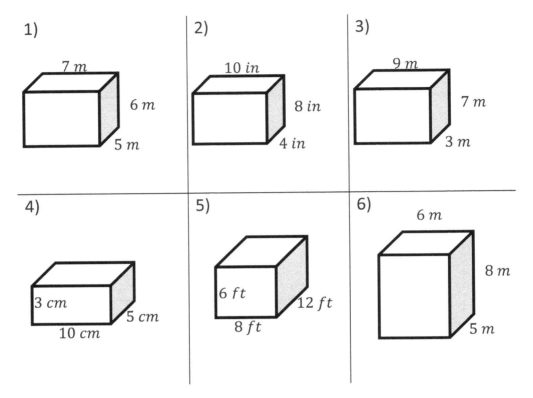

1)   7 m   6 m   5 m

2)   10 in   8 in   4 in

3)   9 m   7 m   3 m

4)   3 cm   5 cm   10 cm

5)   6 ft   12 ft   8 ft

6)   6 m   8 m   5 m

✍ *Find the surface area of each Rectangular Prism.*

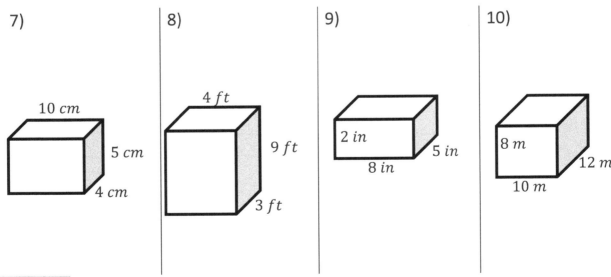

7)   10 cm   5 cm   4 cm

8)   4 ft   9 ft   3 ft

9)   2 in   5 in   8 in

10)   8 m   12 m   10 m

Cylinder

Find the volume of each Cylinder. Round your answer to the nearest tenth. ($\pi = 3.14$)

1)

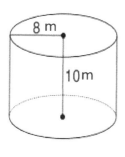

8 m

10m

2)

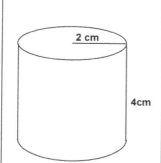

2 cm

4cm

3)

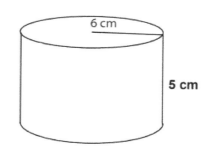

6 cm

5 cm

4)

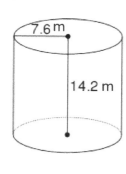

7.6 m

14.2 m

5)

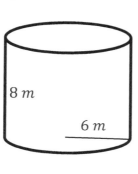

8 m

6 m

6)

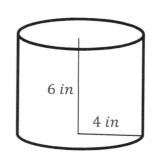

6 in

4 in

Find the surface area of each Cylinder. ($\pi = 3.14$)

7)

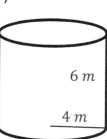

6 m

4 m

8)

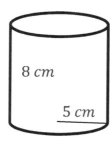

8 cm

5 cm

9)

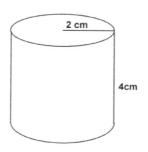

2 cm

4cm

10)

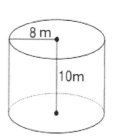

8 m

10m

bit.ly/37LtcVM

Find more at

Answers – Chapter 9

Pythagorean Theorem

1) Yes   7) Yes   13) 5

2) Yes   8) Yes   14) 30

3) No   9) 5   15) 30

4) Yes   10) 17   16) 12

5) No   11) 15

6) No   12) 8

Triangles

1) $15°$ 5) $25°$ 9) 24 *square unites*
2) $35°$ 6) $45°$ 10) 30 *square unites*
3) $15°$ 7) $55°$ 11) 64 *square centimeters*
4) $65°$ 8) $70°$ 12) 20 *square inches*

Polygons

1) 48 *ft*   6) 20 *cm*   10) 80 in^2
2) 36 *in*   7) 18 *in*   11) 35 km^2
3) 48 *ft*   8) 24 *m*   12) 49 in^2
4) 56 *cm*   9) 36 m^2
5) 30 *m*

Circles

1) 43.96 *in*   5) 113.04 *cm*   9) 157 *m*
2) 75.36 *cm*   6) 94.2 *miles*   10) 175.84 *m*
3) 87.92 *ft*   7) 119.32 *in*   11) 219.8 *in*
4) 81.64 *m*   8) 138.16 *ft*   12) 314 *ft*

	Radius	Diameter	Circumference	Area
Circle 1	2 inches	4 inches	12.56 inches	12.56 square inches
Circle 2	4 meters	8 meters	25.12 meters	50.24 square meters
Circle 3	6 ft	12 ft	37.68	113.04 square ft
Circle 4	8 miles	16 miles	50.24 miles	200.96 square miles
Circle 5	4.5 km	9 km	28.26 km	63.585 square km
Circle 6	7 cm	14 cm	43.96 cm	153.86 square cm
Circle 7	5 feet	10 feet	31.4 feet	78.5 square feet
Circle 8	14 m	28 m	87.92 m	615.44 square meters
Circle 9	13 in	26 in	81.64 inches	530.66 square inches
Circle 10	12 feet	24 feet	75.36 feet	452.16 square feet

Trapezoids

1) $63\ cm^2$
2) $160\ m^2$
3) $24\ ft^2$
4) $42.5\ cm^2$

5) 81
6) 94.5
7) 36
8) 18
9) $12\ cm$

10) $5\ ft$
11) $10\ m$
12) $35\ ft$

Cubes

1) $8\ square\ units$
2) $8\ cm^3$
3) $64\ ft^3$
4) $216\ m^3$
5) $1\ in^3$
6) $27\ miles^3$

7) $125\ km^3$
8) $343\ cm^3$
9) $1,000\ ft^3$
10) $1,331\ mm^3$
11) $512\ in^3$
12) $729\ km^3$

13) $24\ square\ units$
14) $150\ m^2$
15) $24\ ft^2$
16) $54\ mm^2$
17) $486\ km^2$
18) $96\ cm^2$

Rectangular Prism

1) $210\ m^3$
2) $320\ in^3$
3) $189\ m^3$
4) $150\ cm^3$

5) $576\ ft^3$
6) $240\ m^3$
7) $220\ cm^2$
8) $150\ ft^2$

9) $132\ in2$
10) $592\ m^2$

Cylinder

1) $2,009.6\ m^3$
2) $50.24\ cm^3$
3) $565.2\ cm^3$
4) $2,575.4\ m^3$

5) $904.3\ m^3$
6) $301.4\ in^3$
7) $251.2\ m^2$
8) $408.2\ cm^2$

9) $75.4\ cm^2$
10) $904.3\ m^2$

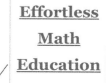

Effortless
Math
Education

Chapter 10: Statistics

Math Topics that you'll learn in this Chapter:

- ✓ Mean, Median,
- ✓ Mode and Range
- ✓ Pie Graph
- ✓ Probability Problems
- ✓ Permutations and Combinations

83

Mean and Median

✍ *Find Mean and Median of the Given Data.*

1) 8, 12, 5, 3, 2

2) 3, 6, 3, 7, 4, 13

3) 13, 5, 1, 7, 9

4) 6, 4, 2, 7, 3, 2

5) 6, 5, 7, 5, 7, 1, 11

6) 6, 1, 4, 4, 9, 2, 16

7) 12, 4, 1, 5, 9, 7, 7, 19

8) 18, 9, 5, 4, 9, 6, 12

9) 28, 25, 15, 16, 32, 44, 71

10) 10, 5, 1, 5, 4, 5, 8, 10

11) 18, 15, 30, 64, 42, 11

12) 44, 33, 56, 78, 41, 84

✍ *Solve.*

13) In a javelin throw competition, five athletics score **56, 58, 63, 57** and **61** meters. What are their Mean and Median? _____

14) Eva went to shop and bought **3** apples, **5** peaches, **8** bananas, **1** pineapple and **3** melons. What are the Mean and Median of her purchase? _____

15) Bob has **12** black pen, **14** red pen, **15** green pens, **24** blue pens and **3** boxes of yellow pens. If the Mean and Median of the number of pens for each color are **16** and **15** respectively, what is the number of yellow pens in each box? _____

Mode and Range

📝 *Find Mode and Rage of the Given Data.*

1) $8, 2, 5, 9, 1, 2$

Mode: _____   Range: _____

2) $6, 6, 2, 3, 6, 3, 9, 12$

Mode: _____   Range: _____

3) $4, 4, 3, 9, 7, 9, 4, 6, 4$

Mode: _____   Range: _____

4) $12, 9, 2, 9, 3, 2, 9, 5$

Mode: _____   Range: _____

5) $9, 5, 9, 5, 8, 9, 8$

Mode: _____   Range: _____

6) $0, 1, 4, 10, 9, 2, 9, 1, 5, 1$

Mode: _____   Range: _____

7) $6, 5, 6, 9, 7, 7, 5, 4, 3, 5$

Mode: _____   Range: _____

8) $7, 5, 4, 9, 6, 7, 7, 5, 2$

Mode: _____   Range: _____

9) $2, 2, 5, 6, 2, 4, 7, 6, 4, 9$

Mode: _____   Range: _____

10) $7, 5, 2, 5, 4, 5, 8, 10$

Mode: _____   Range: _____

11) $4, 1, 5, 2, 2, 12, 18, 2$

Mode: _____   Range: _____

12) $6, 3, 5, 9, 6, 6, 3, 12$

Mode: _____   Range: _____

📝 *Solve.*

13) A stationery sold 12 pencils, 36 red pens, 44 blue pens, 12 notebooks, 18 erasers, 34 rulers and 32 color pencils. What are the Mode and Range for the stationery sells?

Mode: _____   Range: _____

14) In an English test, eight students score $14, 13, 17, 11, 19, 20, 14$ and 15. What are their Mode and Range? _____

15) What is the range of the first 6 even numbers greater than 11? _____

Pie Graph

The circle graph below shows all Jason's expenses for last month. Jason spent **$300** on his bills last month.

Answer following questions based on the Pie graph.

Jason's monthly expenses

1- How much did Jason spend on his car last month? _____

2- How much did Jason spend for foods last month? _____

3- How much did Jason spend on his rent last month? _____

4- What fraction is Jason's expenses for his bills and Car out of his total

   expenses last month? _____

5- How much was Jason's total expenses last month? _____

Probability Problems

🖎 *Solve.*

1) A number is chosen at random from **1** to **10**. Find the probability of selecting number **4** or smaller numbers. _____

2) Bag A contains **9** red marbles and **3** green marbles. Bag B contains **9** black marbles and **6** orange marbles. What is the probability of selecting a green marble at random from bag A? What is the probability of selecting a black marble at random from Bag B? _____ _____

3) A number is chosen at random from **1** to **50**. What is the probability of selecting multiples of **10**. _____

4) A card is chosen from a well-shuffled deck of **52** cards. What is the probability that the card will be a king OR a queen? (The deck includes **13** of each suit clubs, diamonds, hearts, and spades) _____

5) A number is chosen at random from **1** to **10**. What is the probability of selecting a multiple of **3**?_____

A spinner, numbered **1–8**, is spun once. What is the probability of spinning...

6) an EVEN number? _____   7) a multiple of 3? _____

8) a PRIME number? _____   9) number 9? _____

Combinations and Permutations

✎ *Calculate the value of each.*

1) 4! = ____

2) 4! × 3! = ____

3) 5! = ____

4) 6! + 3! = ____

5) 7! = ____

6) 8! = ____

7) 4! + 4! = ____

8) 4! − 3! = ____

✎ *Solve each word problems.*

9) Susan is baking cookies. She uses sugar, flour, butter, and eggs. How many different orders of ingredients can she try? _____

10) Jason is planning for his vacation. He wants to go to museum, watch a movie, go to the beach, and play volleyball. How many different ways of ordering are there for him? _____

11) How many 5-digit numbers can be named using the digits 1, 2, 3, 4, and 5 without repetition? _____

12) In how many ways can 5 boys be arranged in a straight line? _____

13) In how many ways can 4 athletes be arranged in a straight line? _____

14) A professor is going to arrange her 7 students in a straight line. In how many ways can she do this? _____

15) How many code symbols can be formed with the letters for the word WHITE? _____

16) In how many ways a team of 8 basketball players can to choose a captain and co-captain? _____

Answers – Chapter 10

Mean and Median

1) Mean: 6, Median: 5
2) Mean: 6, Median: 5
3) Mean: 7, Median: 7
4) Mean: 4, Median: 3.5
5) Mean: 6, Median: 6

6) Mean: 6, Median: 4
7) Mean: 8, Median: 7
8) Mean: 9, Median: 9
9) Mean: 33, Median: 28
10) Mean: 6, Median: 5

11) Mean: 30, Median: 24
12) Mean: 56, Median: 50
13) Mean: 59, Median: 58
14) Mean: 4, Median: 3
15) 5

Mode and Range

1) Mode: 2, Range: 8
2) Mode: 6, Range: 10
3) Mode: 4, Range: 6
4) Mode: 9, Range: 10
5) Mode: 9, Range: 4

6) Mode: 1, Range: 10
7) Mode: 5, Range: 6
8) Mode: 7, Range: 7
9) Mode: 2, Range: 7
10) Mode: 5, Range: 8

11) Mode: 2, Range: 17
12) Mode: 6, Range: 9
13) Mode: 12, Range: 32
14) Mode: 14, Range: 9
15) 10

Pie Graph

1) $550
2) $250
3) $700

4) $\frac{17}{50}$
5) $2,500

Probability Problems

1) $\frac{2}{5}$
2) $\frac{1}{4}, \frac{3}{5}$
3) $\frac{1}{10}$

4) $\frac{2}{13}$
5) $\frac{3}{10}$
6) $\frac{1}{2}$

7) $\frac{1}{4}$
8) $\frac{1}{2}$
9) 0

Combinations and Permutations

1) 24
2) 144
3) 120
4) 726
5) 5,040
6) 40,320

7) 48
8) 18
9) 24
10) 24
11) 120
12) 120

13) 24
14) 5,040
15) 120
16) 56

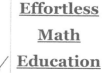

Effortless Math Education

Time to Test

Time to refine your skill with a practice examination

Take practice ISEE Middle Level Math Tests to simulate the test day experience. After you've finished, score your tests using the answer keys.

Before You Start

- You'll need a pencil and a timer to take the test.

- After you've finished the test, review the answer key to see where you went wrong.

- Use the answer sheet provided to record your answers. (You can cut it out or photocopy it)

- Students receive 1 point for every correct answer. There is no penalty for wrong or skipped questions.

Calculators are NOT permitted for the ISEE Middle Level Test

Good Luck!

ISEE Middle Level Math

Practice Test 1

2022 - 2023

Two Parts

Total number of questions: 84

Part 1 (Quantitative Reasoning): 37 questions

Part 2 (Mathematics Achievement): 47 questions

Total time for two parts: 75 Minutes

ISEE Middle Level Practice Test Answer Sheets

Remove (or photocopy) this answer sheet and use it to complete the practice test.

ISEE Middle Level Practice Test 1

Quantitative Reasoning

1 Ⓐ Ⓑ Ⓒ Ⓓ	25 Ⓐ Ⓑ Ⓒ Ⓓ	1 Ⓐ Ⓑ Ⓒ Ⓓ	25 Ⓐ Ⓑ Ⓒ Ⓓ
2 Ⓐ Ⓑ Ⓒ Ⓓ	26 Ⓐ Ⓑ Ⓒ Ⓓ	2 Ⓐ Ⓑ Ⓒ Ⓓ	26 Ⓐ Ⓑ Ⓒ Ⓓ
3 Ⓐ Ⓑ Ⓒ Ⓓ	27 Ⓐ Ⓑ Ⓒ Ⓓ	3 Ⓐ Ⓑ Ⓒ Ⓓ	27 Ⓐ Ⓑ Ⓒ Ⓓ
4 Ⓐ Ⓑ Ⓒ Ⓓ	28 Ⓐ Ⓑ Ⓒ Ⓓ	4 Ⓐ Ⓑ Ⓒ Ⓓ	28 Ⓐ Ⓑ Ⓒ Ⓓ
5 Ⓐ Ⓑ Ⓒ Ⓓ	29 Ⓐ Ⓑ Ⓒ Ⓓ	5 Ⓐ Ⓑ Ⓒ Ⓓ	29 Ⓐ Ⓑ Ⓒ Ⓓ
6 Ⓐ Ⓑ Ⓒ Ⓓ	30 Ⓐ Ⓑ Ⓒ Ⓓ	6 Ⓐ Ⓑ Ⓒ Ⓓ	30 Ⓐ Ⓑ Ⓒ Ⓓ
7 Ⓐ Ⓑ Ⓒ Ⓓ	31 Ⓐ Ⓑ Ⓒ Ⓓ	7 Ⓐ Ⓑ Ⓒ Ⓓ	31 Ⓐ Ⓑ Ⓒ Ⓓ
8 Ⓐ Ⓑ Ⓒ Ⓓ	32 Ⓐ Ⓑ Ⓒ Ⓓ	8 Ⓐ Ⓑ Ⓒ Ⓓ	32 Ⓐ Ⓑ Ⓒ Ⓓ
9 Ⓐ Ⓑ Ⓒ Ⓓ	33 Ⓐ Ⓑ Ⓒ Ⓓ	9 Ⓐ Ⓑ Ⓒ Ⓓ	33 Ⓐ Ⓑ Ⓒ Ⓓ
10 Ⓐ Ⓑ Ⓒ Ⓓ	34 Ⓐ Ⓑ Ⓒ Ⓓ	10 Ⓐ Ⓑ Ⓒ Ⓓ	34 Ⓐ Ⓑ Ⓒ Ⓓ
11 Ⓐ Ⓑ Ⓒ Ⓓ	35 Ⓐ Ⓑ Ⓒ Ⓓ	11 Ⓐ Ⓑ Ⓒ Ⓓ	35 Ⓐ Ⓑ Ⓒ Ⓓ
12 Ⓐ Ⓑ Ⓒ Ⓓ	36 Ⓐ Ⓑ Ⓒ Ⓓ	12 Ⓐ Ⓑ Ⓒ Ⓓ	36 Ⓐ Ⓑ Ⓒ Ⓓ
13 Ⓐ Ⓑ Ⓒ Ⓓ	37 Ⓐ Ⓑ Ⓒ Ⓓ	13 Ⓐ Ⓑ Ⓒ Ⓓ	37 Ⓐ Ⓑ Ⓒ Ⓓ
14 Ⓐ Ⓑ Ⓒ Ⓓ		14 Ⓐ Ⓑ Ⓒ Ⓓ	38 Ⓐ Ⓑ Ⓒ Ⓓ
15 Ⓐ Ⓑ Ⓒ Ⓓ		15 Ⓐ Ⓑ Ⓒ Ⓓ	39 Ⓐ Ⓑ Ⓒ Ⓓ
16 Ⓐ Ⓑ Ⓒ Ⓓ		16 Ⓐ Ⓑ Ⓒ Ⓓ	40 Ⓐ Ⓑ Ⓒ Ⓓ
17 Ⓐ Ⓑ Ⓒ Ⓓ		17 Ⓐ Ⓑ Ⓒ Ⓓ	41 Ⓐ Ⓑ Ⓒ Ⓓ
18 Ⓐ Ⓑ Ⓒ Ⓓ		18 Ⓐ Ⓑ Ⓒ Ⓓ	42 Ⓐ Ⓑ Ⓒ Ⓓ
19 Ⓐ Ⓑ Ⓒ Ⓓ		19 Ⓐ Ⓑ Ⓒ Ⓓ	43 Ⓐ Ⓑ Ⓒ Ⓓ
20 Ⓐ Ⓑ Ⓒ Ⓓ		20 Ⓐ Ⓑ Ⓒ Ⓓ	44 Ⓐ Ⓑ Ⓒ Ⓓ
21 Ⓐ Ⓑ Ⓒ Ⓓ		21 Ⓐ Ⓑ Ⓒ Ⓓ	45 Ⓐ Ⓑ Ⓒ Ⓓ
22 Ⓐ Ⓑ Ⓒ Ⓓ		22 Ⓐ Ⓑ Ⓒ Ⓓ	46 Ⓐ Ⓑ Ⓒ Ⓓ
23 Ⓐ Ⓑ Ⓒ Ⓓ		23 Ⓐ Ⓑ Ⓒ Ⓓ	47 Ⓐ Ⓑ Ⓒ Ⓓ
24 Ⓐ Ⓑ Ⓒ Ⓓ		24 Ⓐ Ⓑ Ⓒ Ⓓ	

Mathematics Achievement

ISEE Middle Level Math

Practice Test 1

Section 1

37 questions

Total time for this section: 35 Minutes

You may NOT use a calculator for this test.

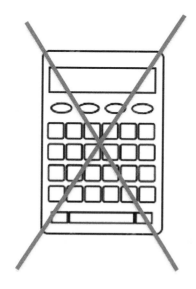

1) If the ratio of home fans to visiting fans in a crowd is $3:2$ and all 25,000 seats in a stadium are filled, how many visiting fans are in attendance?

A. 100,000

B. 10,000

C. 1,000

D. 100

2) In following shape y equals to?

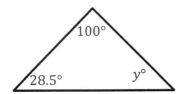

A. 128.5°

B. 51.5°

C. 48.5°

D. 35°

3) Multiply:

$$(2x - 3)(3x + 4)$$

A. $6x^2 - x - 12$

B. $6x^2 + x - 12$

C. $6x^2 + x + 12$

D. $6x^2 - 17x - 12$

4) If an object travels at 0.3 cm per second, how many meters does it travel in 4 hours?

A. 88.2 m

B. 66.4 m

C. 50 m

D. 43.2 m

5) Two fair six-sided dice are thrown. What is the probability that the product is less than or equal to 5?

A. $\frac{1}{8}$

B. $\frac{5}{36}$

C. $\frac{7}{36}$

D. $\frac{5}{18}$

6) Ava uses a 40% off coupon when buying a sweater that costs $40. If she also pays 5% sales tax on the purchase, how much does she pay?

A. $26.95

B. $25.20

C. $21.7

D. $14.83

7) In following Figure, the radius of the circle is $\frac{3}{2}$. If a line segment is drawn inside the circle so it does not extend beyond the circle's outer edge, which of the following can be the line segment length?

A. 3

B. $\frac{14}{3}$

C. 6

D. 8

8) What is the equation of the line through point $(7, -3)$ that has slope $-\frac{1}{4}$?

A. $y = -4x - \frac{5}{4}$

B. $y = -\frac{1}{4}x - \frac{5}{4}$

C. $y = -\frac{1}{4}x - \frac{25}{4}$

D. $y = -4x - \frac{25}{4}$

9) What is the area of the shaded region? (one forth of the circle is shaded)

Diameter $= 12$

A. 6π

B. 7π

C. 8π

D. 9π

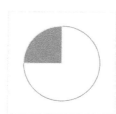

10) If a car has 80-liter petrol and after one hour driving the car use 6-liter petrol, how much petrol remaining after x-hours?

A. $6x - 80$

B. $80 + 6x$

C. $80 - 6x$

D. $80 - x$

11) A shirt costing $200 is discounted 15%. After a month, the shirt is discounted another 15%. Which of the following expressions can be used to find the selling price of the shirt

A. $(200)(0.70)$

B. $(200) - 200(0.30)$

C. $(200)(0.15) - (200)(0.15)$

D. $(200)(0.85)(0.85)$

12) Find $\frac{1}{3}$ of $\frac{2}{5}$ of $\frac{3}{4}$ of 300?

A. 30

B. 32

C. 35

D. 45

13) If $x \le a$ is the solution of $7 + 2x \le 15$, what is the value of a?

A. $14x$

B. 4

C. -4

D. $15x$

14) What is the point of intersection for the following two lines?

$$y = \frac{18}{5}x + 11$$

$$y = -\frac{2}{5}x + 3$$

A. $\left(-2, \frac{4}{5}\right)$

B. $\left(-2, \frac{19}{5}\right)$

C. $\left(2, \frac{19}{5}\right)$

D. $\left(-4, \frac{19}{5}\right)$

15) Solve for x: $3 + x + 6\left(\frac{x}{2}\right) = 2x + 10$

A. $\frac{13}{6}$

B. $\frac{7}{6}$

C. $\frac{7}{2}$

D. $\frac{13}{2}$

16) 6 liters of water are poured into an aquarium that's $15cm$ long, $5cm$ wide, and $90cm$ high. How many cm will the water level in the aquarium rise due to this added water?
($1\ liter\ of\ water = 1,000\ cm^3$)

A. 80

B. 40

C. 20

D. 10

17) If $3f + 2g = 3x + y$ and $g = 2y - 3x$, what is f?

A. $3x + y$

B. $x + 3y$

C. $3x - y$

D. $y - 3x$

18) What is the perimeter of the following parallelogram?

A. 48

B. 34

C. 24

D. 17

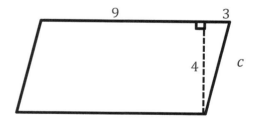

19) In a bundle of 40 fruits, 8 are apples and the rest are bananas. What percent of the bundle is composed of apples?

A. 40%

B. 25%

C. 20%

D. 15%

20) What is the value of $\dfrac{-\frac{11}{2} \times \frac{3}{5}}{\frac{11}{30}}$?

A. -9

B. 9

C. $-\dfrac{1}{9}$

D. $\dfrac{1}{9}$

21) What is the x-intercept of the line represented by the following equation? $y = 4x - 16$

A. -16

B. -12

C. 0

D. 4

22) What is the value of mode and median in the following set of numbers?

$$1, 2, 2, 5, 4, 4, 3, 3, 3, 1, 1$$

A. Mode: $1, 2$ Median: 2

B. Mode: $1, 3$ Median: 3

C. Mode: $2, 3$ Median: 2

D. Mode: $1, 3$ Median: 2.5

23) The ordered pair $(2, -3)$ is in which quadrant?

A. Quadrant I

B. Quadrant II

C. Quadrant III

D. Quadrant IV

24) The members of set A are defined as the values for: $f(x) = 3x^2 + 5$ For vales of x between 5 and 20. What is the range of set A?

A. 16

B. $1,125$

C. $1,205$

D. $1,280$

25) Which is the equivalent temperature of $104°F$ in Celsius? ($C = Celsius$)

$$C = \frac{5}{9}(F - 32)$$

A. 32

B. 38

C. 40

D. 44

Quantitative Comparisons

Direction: Questions 26 to 37 are Quantitative Comparisons Questions. Using the information provided in each question, compare the quantity in column A to the quantity in Column B. Choose on your answer sheet grid

A   if the quantity in Column A is greater

B   if the quantity in Column B is greater

C   if the two quantities are equal

D   if the relationship cannot be determined from the information given

26) A computer costs $270

Column A	Column B
A sales tax at 9% of the computer cost	$24.3

27)

Column A	Column B
$3^2 - 5^4$	$3^4 - 5^2$

28) Which is greater quantity?

Column A	Column B
The perimeter of a right triangle with legs of length 6 inches and 8 inches	Two feet

29)

Column A	Column B
$\dfrac{\sqrt{81-49}}{\sqrt{16-9}}$	$\dfrac{(9-7)}{(4-3)}$

30) Seven cards numbered 1 − 7 are put into a bag.

Column A	Column B
Probability of choosing a number multiple of 2	Probability of choosing a number multiple of 3

31) The sum of 3 consecutive integers is 54.

Column A	Column B
The largest of these integers	20

32)

Column A	Column B
The slope of the line $-4x + 4y = 1$	The slope of the line that passes through points $(3, 5)$ and $(1, 3)$

33) 10 percent of x is equal to 8 percent of y, where x and y are positive numbers.

Column A	Column B
x	y

34) Which is the greater quantity?

Column A	Column B
The reciprocal of 2	The reciprocal of 0.3

35)

Column A	Column B
The least prime factor of 22	The least prime factor of 32

36)

Column A	Column B
$(1.25)^2(1.25)^6$	$(1.25)^8$

37) x is a positive number.

Column A	Column B
x^6	x^{11}

ISEE Middle Level Math

Practice Test 1

Section 2

47 questions

Total time for this section: 40 Minutes

You may NOT use a calculator for this test.

1) If x = lowest common multiple of 30 and 35, then $\frac{x}{2} + 1$ equal to?

A. 210

B. 108

C. 106

D. 96

2) Which of the following is a possible value for x?

$$14.1 < \sqrt{x} < 14.25$$

A. 196

B. 201

C. 210

D. 212

3) Which of the following is not synonym for 10^2?

A. 10 cubed

B. 10 squared

C. The square of 10

D. 10 to the second power

4) If angles A , B and C are angles of a parallelogram, what is the sum of the measures of the three angles?

A. 360 $degrees$

B. 180 $degrees$

C. 90 $degrees$

D. Cannot be determined

5) A swing moves from one extreme point (point A) to the opposite extreme point (point B) in 30 seconds. How long does it take that the swing moves 10 times from point A to point B and returns to point A?

A. 600 $seconds$

B. 300 $seconds$

C. 200 $seconds$

D. 100 $seconds$

6) There are 2 cars moving in the same direction on a road. A red car is $10\ km$ ahead of a blue car. If the speed of the red car is $50\ km\ per\ hour$ and the speed of the blue car is $1\frac{2}{5}$ of the red car, how many minutes will it take the blue car to catch the red car?

A. 8.5

B. 15

C. 30

D. 60

7) Suppose you know the values of x, y and z, and you want to evaluate the expression below.

$(\frac{x}{2})^2 + y \div z$, Which of the following is the first step you must complete?

A. $(\frac{x}{2})^2$

B. $y \div z$

C. $\frac{x}{2} + y$

D. y^2

8) Ten years ago, Lily was half the age of her brother. If her brother is 30 years old now, how old was Lily ten years ago?

A. 10

B. 12

C. 15

D. 18

9) In 1999, the average worker's income increased $2,000 per year starting from $24,000 annual salary. Which equation represents income greater than average?

$(I = \text{income}, x = \text{number of years after 1999})$

A. $I > 2,000x + 24,000$

B. $I > -2,000x + 24,000$

C. $I < -2,000x + 24,000$

D. $I < 2,000x - 24,000$

10) Which of the following angles is obtuse?

A. $220\ degrees$

B. $340\ degrees$

C. $79\ degrees$

D. $110\ degrees$

11) Which of the following points will you find on the x-axis?

A. $(0, -5)$

B. $(-5, 0)$

C. $(0, 5)$

D. $(-5, 5)$

12) What is ratio of perimeter of figure A to area of figure B?

A. $\frac{3}{8}$

B. $\frac{8}{3}$

C. $\frac{8}{5}$

D. $\frac{5}{8}$

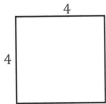

Fig. A

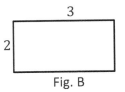

Fig. B

13) What is the greatest common factor of 24, 60 and 72?

A. 4

B. 6

C. 12

D. 16

14) Anita's trick–or–treat bag contains 12 pieces of chocolate, 18 suckers, 18 pieces of gum, 24 pieces of licorice. If she randomly pulls a piece of candy from her bag, what is the probability of her pulling out a piece of sucker

A. $\frac{1}{3}$

B. $\frac{1}{4}$

C. $\frac{1}{6}$

D. $\frac{1}{12}$

15) $\frac{6\ feet + 8\ inches}{4} + \frac{3\ feet + 4\ inches}{2}$ = how many inches?

A. 25 inches

B. 30 inches

C. 32 inches

D. 40 inches

16) Refer to the following graph. If 15,480 people registered for a sports match, how many of them registered for basketball?

A. 774
B. 1,548
C. 2,322
D. 3,096

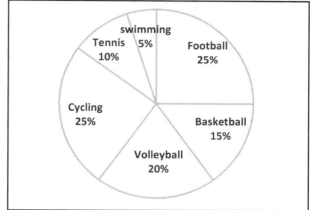

17) 120 is equal to?

A. $20 - (4 \times 10) + (6 \times 30)$

B. $\left(\frac{11}{8} \times 72\right) + (\frac{125}{5})$

C. $\left(\left(\frac{30}{4} + \frac{13}{2}\right) \times 7\right) - \frac{11}{2} + \frac{110}{4}$

D. $(2 \times 10) + (50 \times 1.5) + 15$

18) What is $\frac{5}{8}$ divided by $\frac{5}{32}$?

A. $\frac{1}{4}$

B. 4

C. 5

D. 8

19) When a number is multiplied to itself and added by 10, the result is 35. What is the value of the number?

A. 5 and -5

B. 6 and -6

C. 5

D. 6

20) {3,4,5,8,12} ∩ {2,3,6,8,11,12}

A. {3,8}
B. {8,12}
C. {3,8,12}
D. {3,5,8}

21) How many possible outfit combinations come from six shirts, three slacks, and five ties?

A. 90

B. 60

C. 15

D. 14

22) Which symbol belongs in the box? $\frac{2}{5}$ ☐ $(\frac{1}{5})^2$

A. $=$

B. $\approx$

C. $>$

D. $<$

23) Which of the following is a pair of reciprocals?

A. $(2^3, \frac{1}{2^{-3}})$

B. $(1\frac{1}{4}, \frac{4}{5})$

C. $(3^{10}, 10^3)$

D. $(2\frac{2}{3}, \frac{3}{2})$

24) If $y = 4ab + 3b^3$, what is y when $a = 2$ and $b = 3$?

A. 110

B. 105

C. 81

D. 36

25) The angle of $AOB = 20°$. What fraction of the circle is shaded?

A. $\frac{1}{4}$

B. $\frac{2}{5}$

C. $\frac{2}{6}$

D. $\frac{1}{9}$

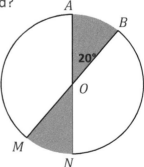

26) In the following equation, what is the value of $x - 2y$?

$$x + 3x - 10 = 2\left(\frac{3}{2}x + y\right) - 15$$

A. 5

B. -25

C. -5

D. 25

27) Write 3,545 in expended form, exponents.

A. $(3 \times 10^2) + (5 \times 10^2) + (45 \times 10)$
B. $(3 \times 10^3) + (5 \times 10) + (4 \times 10) + 5$

C. $(3 \times 10^3) + (5 \times 10^2) + (4 \times 10) + 5$

D. $(3 \times 10^3) + (5 \times 10^2) + (45 \times 10)$

28) Which is **NOT** a prime number?

A. 29

B. 43

C. 47

D. 121

29) A box's width is 1 meter 33 centimeters. How wide is the box in millimeters?

A. 1,300 mm

B. 1,330 mm

C. 11,330 mm

D. 13,300 mm

30) There are three books, a red book, a blue book, and a white book. If the weight of the red book is 80 g and it is 40% of the weight of the blue book, and the weight of the blue book is 125% of the weight of the white book, what is the weight of all three books?

A. 400 g

B. 300 g

C. 250 g

D. 200 g

31) Each of the x students in a team may invite up to 5 friends to a party. What is the maximum number of students and guests who might attend the party?

A. $5x + 5$

B. $5x$

C. $x + 5$

D. $6x$

32) Which of the following is equal to the area of a rectangle with width 2 meters and length 4 meters?

A. $8\ cm^2$

B. $800\ cm^2$

C. $20,000\ cm^2$

D. $80,000\ cm^2$

33) $270\ minutes = \cdots$?

A. $5\ Hours$

B. $4.5\ Hours$

C. $3.5\ Hours$

D. $0.2\ Hours$

34) In the figure below, two lines are parallel. What is the value of angle x?

A. $35\ degree$

B. $92\ degree$

C. $120\ degree$

D. $145\ degree$

35) If R is an odd number, which of the following is always an even number?

A. $\frac{R}{2}$

B. R^2

C. $1 + R$

D. $3R$

36) Adam drove 340 miles and it took him approximately 8 hours. How many miles per hour was his average speed?

A. about 44.5 miles per hour

B. about 42.5 miles per hour

C. about 36.5 miles per hour

D. about 31.5 miles per hour

37) What's the area of the non-shaded part of the following figure? ($\pi = 3$)

A. 27

B. 81

C. 108

D. 110

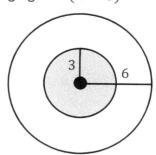

38) What is 21,8210 in scientific notation?

A. 218.21×10^3

B. 21.821×10^4

C. 0.21821×10^6

D. 2.1821×10^5

39) The area of the following right triangle is $50\ cm^2$. Solve for x.

A. 5

B. 8

C. 10

D. $\sqrt{12.5}$

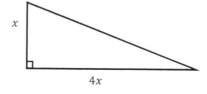

40) What is the probability of rolling an even number, when rolling a normal 6-sided dice?

A. $\frac{1}{6}$

B. $\frac{1}{4}$

C. $\frac{1}{3}$

D. $\frac{1}{2}$

41) The kings are removed from a standard deck of fifty-two cards. What is the probability that a card randomly drawn from that modified deck will be a red 3?

A. $\frac{1}{52}$

B. $\frac{1}{48}$

C. $\frac{1}{24}$

D. $\frac{1}{13}$

42) If x represents the greatest even multiple odd 11 less than 80, and y represents the least odd multiple of 9 greater than 30, what is $x + y$?

A. 111

B. 113

C. 122

D. 145

43) One hundred fifty-three million eight hundred fifty-seven thousand four hundred thirty-two = ?

A. 153,857,432

B. 15,538,574

C. 1,538,574,320

D. 150,538,574

44) Line A passes through the point $(-2, 2)$. Which of the following CANNOT be the equation of line A?

A. $y = x + 4$

B. $y = -x$

C. $y = 3 + x$

D. $\frac{1}{2}x + 3$

45) How much less is the value of $4x - \frac{1}{2}$ than the value of $4x + 2$?

A. 0.5

B. 1

C. 1.5

D. 2.5

46) An angle is equal to one fifth of its supplement. What is the measure of that angle?

A. 20

B. 30

C. 45

D. 60

47) What is the difference of smallest 4–digit number and biggest 4–digit number?

A. 6,666

B. 6,789

C. 8,888

D. 8,999

ISEE Middle Level Math

Practice Test 2

2022 - 2023

Two Parts

Total number of questions: 84

Part 1 (Quantitative Reasoning): 37 questions

Part 2 (Mathematics Achievement): 47 questions

Total time for two parts: 75 Minutes

115

ISEE Middle Level Practice Test Answer Sheets

Remove (or photocopy) this answer sheet and use it to complete the practice test.

ISEE Middle Level Practice Test 2

Quantitative Reasoning   Mathematics Achievement

1 Ⓐ Ⓑ Ⓒ Ⓓ	25 Ⓐ Ⓑ Ⓒ Ⓓ	1 Ⓐ Ⓑ Ⓒ Ⓓ	25 Ⓐ Ⓑ Ⓒ Ⓓ
2 Ⓐ Ⓑ Ⓒ Ⓓ	26 Ⓐ Ⓑ Ⓒ Ⓓ	2 Ⓐ Ⓑ Ⓒ Ⓓ	26 Ⓐ Ⓑ Ⓒ Ⓓ
3 Ⓐ Ⓑ Ⓒ Ⓓ	27 Ⓐ Ⓑ Ⓒ Ⓓ	3 Ⓐ Ⓑ Ⓒ Ⓓ	27 Ⓐ Ⓑ Ⓒ Ⓓ
4 Ⓐ Ⓑ Ⓒ Ⓓ	28 Ⓐ Ⓑ Ⓒ Ⓓ	4 Ⓐ Ⓑ Ⓒ Ⓓ	28 Ⓐ Ⓑ Ⓒ Ⓓ
5 Ⓐ Ⓑ Ⓒ Ⓓ	29 Ⓐ Ⓑ Ⓒ Ⓓ	5 Ⓐ Ⓑ Ⓒ Ⓓ	29 Ⓐ Ⓑ Ⓒ Ⓓ
6 Ⓐ Ⓑ Ⓒ Ⓓ	30 Ⓐ Ⓑ Ⓒ Ⓓ	6 Ⓐ Ⓑ Ⓒ Ⓓ	30 Ⓐ Ⓑ Ⓒ Ⓓ
7 Ⓐ Ⓑ Ⓒ Ⓓ	31 Ⓐ Ⓑ Ⓒ Ⓓ	7 Ⓐ Ⓑ Ⓒ Ⓓ	31 Ⓐ Ⓑ Ⓒ Ⓓ
8 Ⓐ Ⓑ Ⓒ Ⓓ	32 Ⓐ Ⓑ Ⓒ Ⓓ	8 Ⓐ Ⓑ Ⓒ Ⓓ	32 Ⓐ Ⓑ Ⓒ Ⓓ
9 Ⓐ Ⓑ Ⓒ Ⓓ	33 Ⓐ Ⓑ Ⓒ Ⓓ	9 Ⓐ Ⓑ Ⓒ Ⓓ	33 Ⓐ Ⓑ Ⓒ Ⓓ
10 Ⓐ Ⓑ Ⓒ Ⓓ	34 Ⓐ Ⓑ Ⓒ Ⓓ	10 Ⓐ Ⓑ Ⓒ Ⓓ	34 Ⓐ Ⓑ Ⓒ Ⓓ
11 Ⓐ Ⓑ Ⓒ Ⓓ	35 Ⓐ Ⓑ Ⓒ Ⓓ	11 Ⓐ Ⓑ Ⓒ Ⓓ	35 Ⓐ Ⓑ Ⓒ Ⓓ
12 Ⓐ Ⓑ Ⓒ Ⓓ	36 Ⓐ Ⓑ Ⓒ Ⓓ	12 Ⓐ Ⓑ Ⓒ Ⓓ	36 Ⓐ Ⓑ Ⓒ Ⓓ
13 Ⓐ Ⓑ Ⓒ Ⓓ	37 Ⓐ Ⓑ Ⓒ Ⓓ	13 Ⓐ Ⓑ Ⓒ Ⓓ	37 Ⓐ Ⓑ Ⓒ Ⓓ
14 Ⓐ Ⓑ Ⓒ Ⓓ		14 Ⓐ Ⓑ Ⓒ Ⓓ	38 Ⓐ Ⓑ Ⓒ Ⓓ
15 Ⓐ Ⓑ Ⓒ Ⓓ		15 Ⓐ Ⓑ Ⓒ Ⓓ	39 Ⓐ Ⓑ Ⓒ Ⓓ
16 Ⓐ Ⓑ Ⓒ Ⓓ		16 Ⓐ Ⓑ Ⓒ Ⓓ	40 Ⓐ Ⓑ Ⓒ Ⓓ
17 Ⓐ Ⓑ Ⓒ Ⓓ		17 Ⓐ Ⓑ Ⓒ Ⓓ	41 Ⓐ Ⓑ Ⓒ Ⓓ
18 Ⓐ Ⓑ Ⓒ Ⓓ		18 Ⓐ Ⓑ Ⓒ Ⓓ	42 Ⓐ Ⓑ Ⓒ Ⓓ
19 Ⓐ Ⓑ Ⓒ Ⓓ		19 Ⓐ Ⓑ Ⓒ Ⓓ	43 Ⓐ Ⓑ Ⓒ Ⓓ
20 Ⓐ Ⓑ Ⓒ Ⓓ		20 Ⓐ Ⓑ Ⓒ Ⓓ	44 Ⓐ Ⓑ Ⓒ Ⓓ
21 Ⓐ Ⓑ Ⓒ Ⓓ		21 Ⓐ Ⓑ Ⓒ Ⓓ	45 Ⓐ Ⓑ Ⓒ Ⓓ
22 Ⓐ Ⓑ Ⓒ Ⓓ		22 Ⓐ Ⓑ Ⓒ Ⓓ	46 Ⓐ Ⓑ Ⓒ Ⓓ
23 Ⓐ Ⓑ Ⓒ Ⓓ		23 Ⓐ Ⓑ Ⓒ Ⓓ	47 Ⓐ Ⓑ Ⓒ Ⓓ
24 Ⓐ Ⓑ Ⓒ Ⓓ		24 Ⓐ Ⓑ Ⓒ Ⓓ	

ISEE Middle Level Math

Practice Test 2

Section 1

37 questions

Total time for this section: 35 Minutes

You may NOT use a calculator for this test.

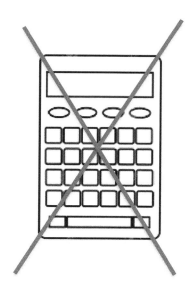

1) Which of the following shows the numbers in increasing order?

A. $\frac{1}{6}, \frac{2}{5}, \frac{1}{3}, \frac{3}{4}$

B. $\frac{1}{6}, \frac{2}{5}, \frac{3}{4}, \frac{1}{3}$

C. $\frac{1}{6}, \frac{1}{3}, \frac{2}{5}, \frac{3}{4}$

D. $\frac{1}{6}, \frac{3}{4}, \frac{1}{3}, \frac{2}{5}$

2) which of the following is equal to $\sqrt{2(4^2) + 2(5^2) + 2(3^2)}$

A. 9

B. 10

C. 11

D. 12

3) Which of the following is equivalent to $\frac{15}{2}t^2$?

A. $6t - \frac{3}{2}t$

B. $\frac{5}{2}t + 3t$

C. $3t.\frac{5}{2}t$

D. $\frac{5}{2}t \div 3t$

4) A $40 shirt now selling for $28 is discounted by what percent?

A. 20%

B. 30%

C. 40%

D. 60%

5) If $f = 2x - 3y$ and $g = x + 4y$, what is $2f + g$?

A. $3x - y$

B. $3x - 2y$

C. $5x - 2y$

D. $5x - y$

6) Consider the data set: $\{20, 20, 30, 30, 40, 40, 40, 40, 50, 60, 60, A\}$

Which of the following elements replaces A to make 41 the mean of the data set?

A. 62

B. 65

C. 70

D. 75

7) According to the following figure, Lisa goes straight from A to B, then goes straight from B to C. Then returns from C to B. What is the ratio of the distance traveled to the perimeter of the triangle?

A. $\frac{5}{6}$

B. $\frac{11}{12}$

C. $\frac{7}{12}$

D. $\frac{1}{4}$

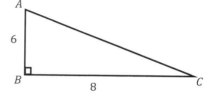

8) The score of Emma was half as that of Ava and the score of Mia was twice that of Ava. If the score of Mia was 60, what is the score of Emma?

A. 15

B. 18

C. 20

D. 30

9) The area of a circle is $64\,\pi$. What is the circumference of the circle?

A. $8\,\pi$

B. $16\,\pi$

C. $32\,\pi$

D. $64\,\pi$

10) Round off the result of 1.12×7.2 to the nearest tenth?

A. 7

B. 8

C. 8.06

D. 8.1

11) The sum of the lengths of 4 sides of a regular pentagon is two feet. What is the perimeter of the pentagon in inches?

A. 20

B. 24

C. 30

D. 32

12) Two third of 18 is equal to $\frac{2}{5}$ of what number?

A. 60

B. 40

C. 35

D. 30

13) In five successive hours, a car traveled $40\ km, 45\ km, 50\ km, 35\ km$ and $65\ km$. In the next five hours, it traveled with an average speed of $50\ km\ per\ hour$. Find the total distance the car traveled in 10 hours.

A. $425\ km$

B. $450\ km$

C. $485\ km$

D. $500\ km$

14) What is the mean in the following set of numbers?

$$9, 12, 29, 36, 45, 63, 99, 123$$

A. 46.2

B. 40.5

C. 59.4

D. 52

15) A box contains thirty-five white marbles, five yellow marbles, ten red marbles, and twenty black marbles, and no other marbles. What is the probability of selecting a marble randomly from this box NOT being white?

A. 1 to 2

B. 1 to 3

C. 2 to 3

D. 1 to 4

16) The price of a laptop is decreased by 10% to $360. What is its original price?

A. $320

B. $380

C. $390

D. $400

17) Find $\frac{1}{4}$ of $\frac{2}{5}$ of 120?

A. 16

B. 12

C. 8

D. 4

18) The ratio of boys and girls in a class is $4 : 7$. If there are 66 students in the class, how many more boys should be enrolled to make the ratio $1 : 1$?

A. 8

B. 10

C. 18

D. 20

19) Which of the following equations best represents the relationship described by the table?

A. $v = h + 7$

B. $v = 8h$

C. $v = 5h + 3$

D. $v = 10h - 2$

Hour (h)	Number of viruses (v)
1	8
2	13
3	18
4	23
5	28

20) A company pays its employee $5,000 plus 2% of all sales profit. If x is all sold profit, which of the following represents the employee's revenue?

A. $0.02x$

B. $0.98x - 5,000$

C. $0.02x + 5,000$

D. $0.98x + 5,000$

21) Which of the following is a correct statement?

A. $\frac{3}{4} > 0.8$

B. $10\% = \frac{2}{5}$

C. $3 < \frac{5}{2}$

D. $\frac{5}{6} > 0.8$

22) What is the value of x in the following figure?

A. 150

B. 145

C. 125

D. 105

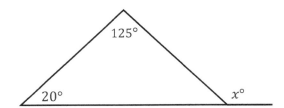

23) There are 80 books in a library. $\frac{3}{4}$ of the books are historical. The rest are literary. If the number of historical books doubled and 10 literary books are removed, what is the ratio of literary books to the total number of books in the newly enlarged quantity of books in the library?

A. $1:3$

B. $1;10$

C. $1;12$

D. $1:13$

24) Anna saves $15.78 per week. Her friend Sarah saves $14.03 per week. After 33 weeks, how much does Anna save more than Sarah?

A. $53.35

B. $57.75

C. $63.15

D. $520.74

25) Car A use 8-liter petrol per 100 kilometers; car B use 6-liter petrol per 100 kilometers. If both cars drive 250 kilometers, how much more petrol does car A use?

A. 5

B. 10

C. 15

D. 20

Quantitative Comparisons

Direction: Questions 26 to 37 are Quantitative Comparisons Questions. Using the information provided in each question, compare the quantity in column A to the quantity in Column B. Choose on your answer sheet grid

A   if the quantity in Column A is greater

B   if the quantity in Column B is greater

C   if the two quantities are equal

D   if the relationship cannot be determined from the information given

26) Which is the greater quantity?

Column A	Column B
The midrange of the data set $\{5,10,15,20,25,30\}$	The midrange of the data set $\{10,20,30,40,50\}$

27) $y = -4x - 8$

Column A	Column B
The value of x when $y = 12$	-4

28) A, B, C and D are points on line R. If $AB = BC = CD$:

Column A	Column B
The distance between A and C	The distance between B and D

29) Monica's saving is $\frac{7}{8}$ of Jennifer's saving and Sandra's saving is $\frac{5}{4}$ of Monica's saving.

Column A	Column B
Jennifer's saving	Sandra's saving

30) Which is the greater quantity?

Column A	Column B
$5t + 4t + 3t - 2t$	$7t + 5t + 2t$

31)

Column A	Column B
Area of a triangle with base 2 and height 10	Four times the area of a square with side 2

32) x is an integer greater than zero.

Column A	Column B
$\dfrac{1}{x} + x$	8

33) $\dfrac{4}{5} < x < \dfrac{6}{7}$

Column A	Column B
x	$\dfrac{5}{6}$

34) x is an integer.

Column A	Column B
$\dfrac{x^6}{6}$	$\left(\dfrac{x}{6}\right)^6$

35) The ratio of blue to black marbles in a basket is 3 to 10.

Column A	Column B
Twice the number of blue marbles in the basket	Half the number of black marbles in the basket

36) $m\angle A_1 = 60°, \angle B = \angle C_1, \angle D = \angle A_2$

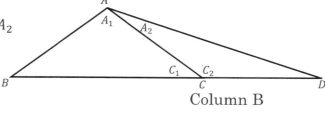

Column A	Column B
$m\angle B$	$m\angle D$

37) $2x^3 + 10 = 64$

$120 - 18y = 84$

Column A	Column B
x	y

IF YOU FINISH BEFORE TIME IS CALLED, YOU MAY CHECK YOUR WORK ON THIS SECTION ONLY. DO NOT TURN TO ANY OTHER SECTION IN THE TEST. **STOP**

ISEE Middle Level Math

Practice Test 2

Section 2

47 questions

Total time for this section: 40 Minutes

You may NOT use a calculator for this test.

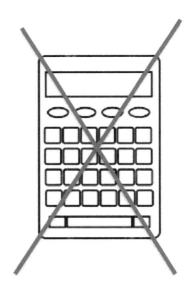

1) What number is 12 more than 15% of 180?

A. 40

B. 39

C. 15

D. 10

2) If the number of red cars to blue cars in a parking lot is in the ratio of $2:5$, how many red cars are there if 90 blue cars are in the parking lot?

A. 72

B. 36

C. 25

D. 10

3) $3\left(\frac{1}{3} - \frac{1}{9}\right) + 1$?

A. 1.5

B. 1.66 …

C. 5.5

D. 5.11 …

4) In a bundle of 90 pencils, 43 are red and the rest are blue. About what percent of the bundle is composed of blue pencils?

A. 62%

B. 58%

C. 54%

D. 52%

5) Which of the following is one value of x in the following equation?

$$(x + 5)^2 = 144$$

A. 1

B. -17

C. -1

D. -7

6) Find the slope of the line that passes through coordinates $(6, -2)$ and $(-6, -4)$

A. $-\frac{1}{12}$

B. $-\frac{1}{6}$

C. $\frac{1}{12}$

D. $\frac{1}{6}$

7) Which is equivalent to the following equation? $x = \frac{2y}{3} - 6$

A. $2y - 3x - 18 = 0$

B. $2x + 3x = -6$

C. $3x + 6 = \frac{2y}{3}$

D. $3x - 2y = -6$

8) The price of a car was $20,000 in 2014, $16,000 in 2015 and $12,800 in 2016. What is the rate of depreciation of the price of car per year?

A. 15%

B. 20%

C. 25%

D. 30%

9) When a number is subtracted from 24 and the difference is divided by that number, the result is 3. What is the value of the number?

A. 2

B. 4

C. 6

D. 12

10) 95 is equal to?

A. $2 + (3 \times 10) + (2 \times 30)$

B. $\left(\frac{10}{3} \times 27\right) + (\frac{5}{2} \times 2)$

C. $\left(\left(\frac{3}{2} + 3\right) \times \frac{18}{3}\right) + 63$

D. $(2 \times 15) + (50 \times 2) - 46$

11) If $\frac{3x}{2} = 60$, then $\frac{2x}{5} = ?$

A. 16

B. 20

C. 25

D. 30

12) Which of the following is the greatest number?

A. $\frac{1}{3}$

B. $\frac{7}{9}$

C. 0.9

D. 85%

13) The surface of a cube is $150 \ cm^2$. What is the volume of the cube?

A. $175 \ cm^3$

B. $125 \ cm^3$

C. $90 \ cm^3$

D. $25 \ cm^3$

14) Which of the following is a whole number followed by its Cube?

A. 3, 30

B. 4, 84

C. 5, 130

D. 6, 216

15) What is the missing term in the given numbers?

$$2, 3, 5, 8, 12, 17, 23, \underline{}, 38$$

A. 24

B. 26

C. 27

D. 30

16) In the diagram below, circle A represents the set of all even numbers, circle B represents the set of all perfect square numbers, and circle C represents the set of all multiples of 10. Which number could be replaced with z?

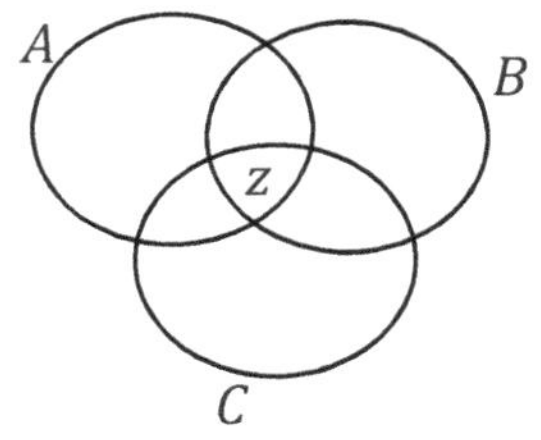

A. 10

B. 16

C. 25

D. 100

17) What is the value of the expression $0.45 + 0.3 + 2.6 + 2.94$?

A. 5.78

B. 6.02

C. 6.29

D. 8.33

18) Mark drinks a glass of water every 45 minutes. In 12 hours, how many times does he drink water?

A. 10

B. 12

C. 15

D. 16

19) Which graph does not represent y as a function of x?

A.

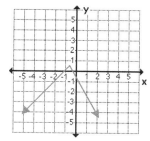

B.

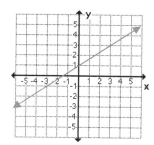

C.

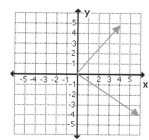

D.

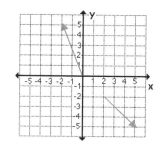

20) Which of the following is equivalent to $13 < -3x - 2 < 22$?

A. $-8 < x < -5$

B. $5 < x < 8$

C. $\frac{11}{3} < x < \frac{20}{3}$

D. $\frac{-20}{3} < x < \frac{-11}{3}$

21) In a certain bookshelf of a library, there are 35 biology books, 95 history books, and 80 language books. What is the ratio of the number of biology books to the total number of books in this bookshelf?

A. $\frac{1}{4}$

B. $\frac{1}{6}$

C. $\frac{2}{7}$

D. $\frac{3}{8}$

22) $185\ minutes\ = ...?$

A. $3.25\ hours$

B. $3.08\ hours$

C. $2\ hours$

D. $1.8\ hours$

23) In the equation $2x - 12 + 4 = 4y$ what is the value of $(2y - x)$?

A. 16

B. 8

C. -4

D. -8

24) Which of the following is **NOT** a prime number?

A. 103

B. 97

C. 79

D. 57

25) What is the perimeter of a square that has an area of 64 square inches?

A. $144\ inches$

B. $64\ inches$

C. $32\ inches$

D. $16\ inches$

26) The surface area of a cube is $150\ m^2$. What is the volume of the cube?

A. $25\ m^3$

B. $100\ m^3$

C. $125\ m^3$

D. $150\ m^3$

27) What proportions must be true if triangle ABC and triangle ADE are similar?

A. $\dfrac{AB}{AD} = \dfrac{BC}{DE}$

B. $\dfrac{AB}{AE} = \dfrac{BC}{DE}$

C. $\dfrac{AE}{AD} = \dfrac{BC}{DE}$

D. $\dfrac{AD}{DB} = \dfrac{BC}{DE}$

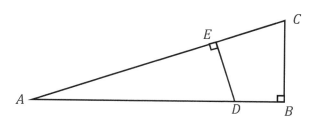

28) Sandra started reading the book at 10:30. She began to rest after 2 hours and 45 minutes of study. She rested for 1 hour and 35 minutes and then went shopping. When did Sandra go shopping?

A. $1:00\ P.M$

B. $1:15\ P.M$

C. $2:50\ P.M$

D. $3:10\ P.M$

29) The width of a rectangle is $4x$ and its length is $6x$. The perimeter of the rectangle is 80. What is the value of x?

A. 4

B. 5

C. 6

D. 10

30) Jason is 9 miles ahead of Joe running at 5.5 miles per hour and Joe is running at the speed of 7 miles per hour. How long does it take Joe to catch Jason?

A. 3 hours

B. 4 hours

C. 6 hours

D. 8 hours

31) $[5 \times (-14) + 8] - (-4) + [4 \times 5] \div 2 = ?$

A. 144

B. 48

C. -144

D. -48

32) Which statement about the number 374,820,159 is NOT true?

A. The digit 7 has a value of (7×10^7)

B. The digit 8 has a value of (8×10^6)

C. The digit 2 has a value of (2×10^3)

D. The digit 1 has a value of (1×10^2)

33) What is an example of a pair of inverse numbers?

A. $6, -6$

B. $5, 6$

C. $5, -\frac{1}{5}$

D. $1, 1$

34) What are the coordinates of point M on the following graph?

A. $(3, 3)$

B. $(6. -5)$

C. $(-5, 3)$

D. $(-5, -5)$

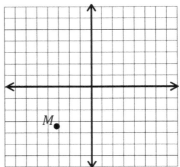

35) Sam draws a shape on his paper. The shape has four sides. It has two pairs of parallel sides and has no right angle. What shape could be Sam's drawing?

A. Trapezoid

B. rectangle

C. Parallelogram

D. Square

36) In the triangle below, if the measure of angle A is 42 degrees, then what is the value of y? (figure is NOT drawn to scale)

A. 40

B. 51

C. 55

D. 87

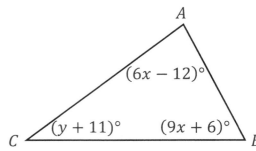

37) In the figure below, what is the area of shaded part?

A. 10

B. 12

C. 15

D. 20

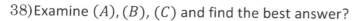

38) Examine $(A), (B), (C)$ and find the best answer?

$(A) = \dfrac{8 \times 4}{2}, (B) = 2^3, (C) = (2 \times 3) + 2$

A. $(A) = (B)$ and $(A) - (B) = (C)$

B. $(B) = (C)$ and $(B) + (C) = (A)$

C. $(B) = (C)$ and $(B) + (C) > (A)$

D. $(A) = (C)$ and $(A) + (C) < (B)$

39) What is the value of x the following equation?

$$6^x = 1{,}296$$

A. 3

B. 4

C. 5

D. 6

40) What is the area of the trapezoid?

A. 25

B. 50

C. 100

D. 200

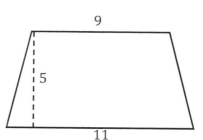

41) $12.124 \div 0.002$?

A. 6.062

B. 60.62

C. 606.2

D. 6,062

42) Use the diagram provided as a reference. If the length between point A and D is 50, $AB = CD$, and the length between point C and D is 20, what is the length between point B and C?

A. 10

B. 15

C. 20

D. 25

43) Ella bought a pair of gloves for $12.49. She gave the clerk $18.00. How much change should she get back?

A. $4.51

B. $5.51

C. $6.51

D. $7.51

44) If 60% of A is 20% of B, then B is what percent of A?

A. 3%

B. 30%

C. 200%

D. 300%

45) A card is drawn at random from a standard 52–card deck, what is the probability that the card is of Hearts? (The deck includes 13 of each suit clubs, diamonds, hearts, and spades)

A. $\frac{1}{3}$

B. $\frac{1}{4}$

C. $\frac{1}{6}$

D. $\frac{1}{52}$

46) $\frac{3}{4} + \frac{\frac{-2}{5}}{\frac{4}{10}} = ?$

A. $\frac{1}{4}$

B. $\frac{1}{2}$

C. $-\frac{1}{4}$

D. $-\frac{1}{2}$

47) Which of the following equations that students have written is false?

Martha wrote $3\frac{1}{2} = \frac{7}{2}$

Rachel wrote $4\frac{2}{5} = \frac{22}{5}$

Donna wrote $3\frac{1}{3} = \frac{10}{9}$

Anna wrote $12.5 = \frac{125}{100}$

A. Anna only

B. Donna only

C. Martha and Rachel only

D. Donna and Anna only

ISEE Middle Level Math Practice Tests Answer Keys

Now, it's time to review your results to see where you went wrong and what areas you need to improve.

ISEE Middle Level Math Practice Test 1 Answer Key								
Quantitative Reasoning				**Mathematics Achievement**				
1 B	17 C	33 B	1 C	17 C	33 B
2 B	18 B	34 B	2 B	18 B	34 D
3 A	19 C	35 B	3 A	19 A	35 C
4 D	20 A	36 C	4 D	20 C	36 B
5 D	21 D	37 A	5 A	21 A	37 B
6 B	22 B		6 C	22 C	38 D
7 A	23 D		7 A	23 B	39 A
8 B	24 B		8 A	24 B	40 D
9 D	25 C		9 A	25 D	41 C
10 C	26 C		10 D	26 C	42 A
11 D	27 A		11 B	27 C	43 A
12 A	28 C		12 B	28 D	44 C
13 B	29 A		13 C	29 B	45 D
14 B	30 A		14 B	30 A	46 B
15 C	31 B		15 D	31 D	47 D
16 A	32 C		16 C	32 D	

ISEE Middle Level Math Practice Test 2 Answer Key

Quantitative Reasoning				Mathematics Achievement		

1 C	17 B	33 D	1 B	17 C	33 D	
2 B	18 C	34 A	2 B	18 D	34 B	
3 C	19 C	35 C	3 B	19 A	35 C	
4 B	20 C	36 C	4 D	20 C	36 A	
5 C	21 D	37 A	5 B	21 C	37 A	
6 A	22 B		6 D	22 A	38 B	
7 B	23 D		7 A	23 D	39 B	
8 A	24 B		8 B	24 D	40 B	
9 B	25 A		9 C	25 C	41 D	
10 D	26 B		10 B	26 C	42 A	
11 C	27 B		11 A	27 B	43 B	
12 D	28 C		12 C	28 C	44 D	
13 C	29 B		13 B	29 A	45 B	
14 D	30 B		14 D	30 C	46 C	
15 A	31 B		15 D	31 D	47 D	
16 D	32 D		16 D	32 C		

Score Your Test

ISEE scores are broken down by its four sections: Verbal Reasoning, Reading Comprehension, Quantitative Reasoning, and Mathematics Achievement. A sum of the three sections is also reported.

For the Middle Level ISEE, the score range is 760 to 940, the lowest possible score a student can earn is 760 and the highest score is 940 for each section. A student receives 1 point for every correct answer. There is no penalty for wrong or skipped questions.

The total scaled score for a Middle Level ISEE test is the sum of the scores for all sections. A student will also receive a percentile score of between 1-99% that compares that student's test scores with those of other test takers of same grade and gender from the past 3 years.

Use the next table to convert ISEE Middle level raw score to scaled score for application to 7th and 8th grade.

ISEE Middle Level Scaled Scores									
Raw Score	Quantitative Reasoning		Mathematics Achievement		Raw Score	Quantitative Reasoning		Mathematics Achievement	
	7th Grade	8th Grade	7th Grade	8th Grade		7th Grade	8th Grade	7th Grade	8th Grade
0	760	760	760	760	26	900	885	885	865
1	770	765	770	765	27	905	890	885	865
2	780	770	780	770	28	910	895	890	870
3	790	775	790	775	29	910	900	890	870
4	800	780	800	780	30	915	905	895	875
5	810	785	810	785	31	920	910	895	875
6	820	790	820	790	32	925	915	900	880
7	825	795	825	795	33	930	920	900	880
8	830	800	830	800	34	930	925	905	885
9	835	805	835	805	35	935	930	905	885
10	840	810	840	810	36	935	935	910	890
11	845	815	845	815	37	940	940	910	890
12	850	820	850	820	38			915	895
13	855	825	855	825	39			920	900
14	860	830	855	830	40			925	905
15	865	835	860	835	41			925	910
16	870	840	860	840	42			930	915
17	875	845	865	840	43			930	920
18	880	845	865	845	44			935	925
19	880	850	870	845	45			935	930
20	885	855	870	850	46			940	935
21	885	860	875	850	47			940	940
22	890	865	875	855					
23	890	870	875	855					
24	895	875	880	860					
25	895	880	880	860					

ISEE Middle Level Math

Practice Tests Answers

and Explanations

ISEE Middle LEVEL Math Practice Test 1 Section 1

1) Choice B is correct

Number of visiting fans: $\frac{2 \times 25,000}{5} = 10,000$

2) Choice B is correct

In triangles sum of all angles equal to $180°$, then:$y = 180° - (100° + 28.5°) =$

$100° - 128.5° = 51.5°$

3) Choice A is correct

$(2x - 3)(3x + 4) = 2x \times (3x + 4) - 3 \times (3x + 4) = 6x^2 + 8x - 9x - 12 = 6x^2 - x - 12$

4) Choice D is correct

One hour equal to 60 minutes then, 4 hours $= 4 \times 60 = 240$ minutes

One minute equal to 60 seconds then, 240 minutes $= 240 \times 60 = 14,400$ seconds

Distance that travel by object is: $0.3 \times 14,400 = 4,320 \, cm = 43.2 \, m$

5) Choice D is correct

Rolls that have a product less than or equal to 5 are:
$(1,1), (1,2), (1,3), (1,4), (1,5), (2,1), (3,1), (4,1), (5,1), (2,2)$

These are 9 out of 36 rolls, so the probability of getting one of them is: $\frac{10}{36} = \frac{5}{18}$

6) Choice B is correct

40% off is: 40% of $\$40 = \frac{40}{100} \times 40 = \$16$, then, the sales price of the sweater is $24.

5% of $\$24 = \frac{5}{100} \times 24 = \$1.20$. Ava pays: $\$24 + \$1.2 = \$25.20$

7) Choice A is correct

The largest length of the line segment is equal to the diameter of the circle:

length of the line segment $\le$ diameter of the circle

diameter of the circle $= 2 \times \frac{3}{2} = 3$. Only choice A can be the length of the line segment.

8) Choice B is correct

Use the point-slope formula with $m = -\frac{1}{4}, x_1 = 7, y_1 = -3$

$$y - y_1 = m(x - x_1) \rightarrow y - (-3) = -\frac{1}{4}(x - 7) \rightarrow y + 3 = -\frac{1}{4}x + \frac{7}{4} \rightarrow y = -\frac{1}{4}x + \frac{7}{4} - 3$$
$$\rightarrow y = -\frac{1}{4}x + \frac{7}{4} - \frac{12}{4} \rightarrow y = -\frac{1}{4}x - \frac{5}{4}$$

9) Choice D is correct

Area of circle with diameter 12 is: $\pi r^2 = \pi \left(\frac{12}{2}\right)^2 = 36\pi$, the area of shaded region is: $\frac{36\pi}{4} = 9\pi$

10) Choice C is correct

The amount of petrol consumed after x hours is: $6x$, Petrol remaining: $80 - 6x$

11) Choice D is correct

To find the discount, multiply the number by $(100\% - rate\ of\ discount)$.

Therefore, for the first discount we get: $(200)(100\% - 15\%) = (200)(0.85)$

For the next 15% discount: $(200)(0.85)(0.85)$

12) Choice A is correct

$\frac{3}{4}$ of $200 = \frac{3}{4} \times 300 = 225$, $\frac{2}{5}$ of $225 = \frac{2}{5} \times 225 = 90$, $\frac{1}{3}$ of $90 = \frac{1}{3} \times 90 = 30$

13) Choice B is correct

$7 + 2x \le 15 \to 2x \le 15 - 7 \to 2x \le 8 \to x \le \frac{8}{2} \to x \le 4$,   Then: $a = 4$

14) Choice B is correct

At the intersection of two lines the x and y values for each equation will be the same. Then:
$\frac{18}{5}x + 11 = -\frac{2}{5}x + 3 \to \frac{18}{5}x + \frac{2}{5}x = 3 - 11 \to \frac{20}{5}x = -8 \to 4x = -8 \to x = -2$

Put $x = -2$ in the line equation: $y = -\frac{2}{5}x + 3 = -\frac{2}{5}(-2) + 3 = \frac{4}{5} + 3 = \frac{4}{5} + \frac{15}{5} = \frac{19}{5}$

15) Choice C is correct

$3 + x + 6\left(\frac{x}{2}\right) = 2x + 10 \to 3 + x + 3x = 2x + 10 \to 2x = 7 \to x = \frac{7}{2}$

16) Choice A is correct

$One\ liter = 1,000\ cm^3 \to 6\ liters = 6,000\ cm^3$, $6,000 = 15 \times 5 \times h \to h = \frac{6,000}{75} = 80\ cm$

17) Choice C is correct

$3f + 2g = 3x + y \to 3f + 2(2y - 3x) = 3x + y \to 3f + 4y - 6x = 3x + y \to$

$3f = 9x - 3y \to f = 3x - y$

18) Choice B is correct

$c = \sqrt{4^2 + 3^2} = \sqrt{25} = 5$

Perimeter of parallelogram$= (9 + 3 + 5) \times 2 = 34$

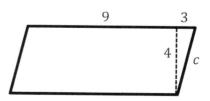

19) Choice C is correct

$$\frac{8}{40} \times 100 = \frac{8}{4} \times 10 = 20\%$$

20) Choice A is correct

$$\frac{-\frac{11}{2} \times \frac{3}{5}}{\frac{11}{30}} = -\frac{\frac{11 \times 3}{2 \times 5}}{\frac{11}{30}} = -\frac{\frac{33}{10}}{\frac{11}{30}} = -\frac{33 \times 30}{11 \times 10} = -9$$

21) Choice D is correct

To find the x-intercept, set the y value to zero and solve for x.

$$0 = 4x - 16 \rightarrow 4x = 16 \rightarrow x = 4$$

22) Choice B is correct

Write the numbers in order: $1, 1, 1, 2, 2, 3, 3, 3, 4, 4, 5$

The mode of numbers is: 1 and 3; median is: 3

23) Choice D is correct

Quadrant I is the top right, and they are numbered counter-clockwise. Since the x-coordinate is 2, we go to the right two unit (starting from Origin of coordinates). Since the y-coordinate is -3, we go to the downward three unit. Therefore, the point $(2, -3)$ is in Quadrant IV.

24) Choice B is correct

To find the range of a set of numbers, we need to subtract the smallest value from the largest. The smallest will be $f(5)$ and the largest will be $f(20)$:

$$f(5) = 3(5)^2 + 5 = 3 \times 25 + 5 = 80$$

$$f(20) = 3(20)^2 + 5 = 3 \times 400 + 5 = 1{,}205$$

Therefore, the range is: $1{,}205 - 80 = 1{,}125$.

25) Choice C is correct

Plug in 104 for F and then solve for C. $C = \frac{5}{9}(F - 32) \Rightarrow C = \frac{5}{9}(104 - 32) \Rightarrow$

$$C = \frac{5}{9}(72) = 40$$

26) Choice C is correct

Column A: 9% of the computer cost is 24.3: $9\% \times 270 = 0.09 \times 270 = 24.3$

Column B: 24.3

27) Choice B is correct.

Column A: $3^2 - 5^4 = 9 - 625 = -616$, Column B: $3^4 - 5^2 = 81 - 25 = 56$

28) Choice C is correct.

The length of the hypotenuse of a triangle with legs 6 inches and 8 inches long is calculated using the Pythagorean Theorem, setting $a = 6, b = 8 \rightarrow c = \sqrt{a^2 + b^2} = \sqrt{6^2 + 8^2} = \sqrt{36 + 64} = \sqrt{100} = 10$. Now calculate the perimeter: $6 + 8 + 10 = 24$, which is equal to two feet.

29) Choice A is correct.

Column A: Simplify. $\frac{\sqrt{81-49}}{\sqrt{16-9}} = \frac{\sqrt{32}}{\sqrt{7}} = \sqrt{\frac{32}{7}}$ which is bigger than 2 ($\sqrt{4} = 2$ and $\frac{32}{7}$ is bigger than 4).

Column B: $\frac{(9-7)}{(4-3)} = \frac{2}{1} = 2$

30) Choice B is correct.

Column B: Simplify. $\sqrt{25 - 9} = \sqrt{16} = 4$

Column A: $\sqrt{25} - \sqrt{9} = 5 - 3 = 2$, $\sqrt{14}$ is bigger than 2. ($\sqrt{4} = 2$)

31) Choice A is correct.

These numbers are in the bag: 1, 2, 3, 4, 5, 6, 7. Quantity A: 2, 4, 6 $\rightarrow \frac{3}{7}$,

Quantity B: 3, 6 $\rightarrow \frac{2}{7}$. So, Quantity A is greater.

32) Choice C is correct.

Column A: Write the equation in slope intercept form. $-4x + 4y = 1 \rightarrow 4y = 4x + 1 \rightarrow$

$y = x + \dfrac{1}{4}$

Column B: The slope of the line that passes through points $(1, 3)$ and $(3, 5)$:

Use slope formula: $slope\ of\ a\ line = \frac{y_2 - y_1}{x_2 - x_1} = \frac{5-3}{3-1} = 1$

33) Choice B is correct

$10\%\ of\ x = 8\%$ of $y \rightarrow 0.1\,x = 0.08\,y \rightarrow x = \frac{0.08}{0.1}y \rightarrow x = \frac{8}{10}y$, therefore, y is bigger than x.

34) Choice B is correct

Quantity A: $(-4)^3 = (-4) \times (-4) \times (-4) = -64$, Quantity B: $4 \times 4 \times 4 = 64$

Quantity B is greater.

35) Choice B is correct

The reciprocal of any fraction can be found by switching numerator and denominator. Column A: 2 will have reciprocal $\frac{1}{2}$. Column B: $0.3 = \frac{3}{10}$ will have reciprocal $\frac{10}{3}$. Compare these by writing them both with common denominator $LCM(2,3) = 6 \rightarrow \frac{1}{2} = \frac{1 \times 3}{2 \times 3} = \frac{3}{6}, \frac{10}{3} = \frac{10 \times 2}{3 \times 2} = \frac{20}{6} \rightarrow \frac{1}{2} = \frac{3}{6} < \frac{10}{3} = \frac{20}{6}$

36) Choice C is correct.

Use exponent "product rule": $x^n \times x^m = x^{n+m}$, Quantity A: $(1.25)^2(1.25)^6 = (1.25)^{2+6} = (1.25)^8$, Quantity B: $(1.25)^8$, The two quantities are equal.

37) Choice D is correct.

Plug in different values for x and check quantity A and B. Let's choose 1 for x. Then:

Quantity A: $x^6 = 1^6 = 1$; Quantity B: $x^{11} = 1^{11} = 1$

Now, let's choose 2 for x. Then: $2^6 < 2^{11}$

The relationship cannot be determined from the information given

ISEE Middle LEVEL Math Practice Test 1 Section 2

1) Choice C is correct

Prime factorizing of $30 = 2 \times 3 \times 5$, Prime factorizing of $35 = 5 \times 7$

$x = LCM = 2 \times 3 \times 5 \times 7 = 210, \frac{210}{2} + 1 = 105 + 1 = 106$

2) Choice B is correct

We can find more information on the value of x by squaring all of our terms to remove the square root: $14.1^2 < (\sqrt{x})^2 < 14.25^2 \rightarrow 198.81 < x < 203.06$

Only choice B is a possible value for x.

3) Choice A is correct

10 cubed is: $10^3 = 1,000$

4) Choice D is correct

All angles in a parallelogram sum up to 360 degrees. Since, we only have 3 angles, therefore the answer cannot be determined.

5) Choice A is correct

Swing moves once from point A to point B and returns to point A is: $30 + 30 = 60 \ seconds$

Therefore, for ten times: $10 \times 60 = 600$ seconds

6) Choice C is correct

$1\frac{2}{5} = \frac{7}{5} = 1.4$, Speed of the blue car: $1.4 \times 50 = 70$, Difference of the cars' speed:

$70 - 50 = 20$, The red car is $10 \ km$ ahead of a blue car. Therefore, it takes the blue car 30 minutes to catch the red car. $\frac{10}{20} = 0.5$ Hour $= 30$ minutes

7) Choice A is correct

Use the order of operations, PEMDAS: Parentheses, Exponents, Multiplication, Division, Addition, Subtraction. In our expression, we have a parenthesis which is the first step to simplify the expression: $(\frac{x}{2})^2$

8) Choice A is correct

Because Lily's brother is now 30, ten years ago he was 20. Lily was half the age of her brother, or $\frac{1}{2} \times 20 = 10$.

9) Choice A is correct

Let x be the number of years. Therefore, \$2,000 per year equals $2,000x$. starting from \$24,000 annual salary means you should add that amount to $2,000x$. Income more than that is: $I > 2,000 \ x + 24,000$

10) Choice D is correct

Angle between 90° and 180° is called obtuse angle.

11) Choice B is correct

A point is located on the x-axis if and only if it has y-coordinate (second coordinate) 0. Of the four choices, only $(-5, 0)$ fits that description.

12) Choice B is correct

Perimeter $A = 4 \times 4 = 16$, Area $B = 2 \times 3 = 6$, $\frac{16}{6} = \frac{8}{3}$

13) Choice C is correct

First factor the numbers as a product of prime numbers:

$24 := 2 \times 2 \times 2 \times 3$

$60 := 2 \times 2 \times 3 \times 5$

$72 := 2 \times 2 \times 2 \times 3 \times 3$

Now take all of the factors that are in common between $24, 60$ and 72.

$GCF = 2 \times 2 \times 3 = 12$

14) Choice B is correct

$Probability = \frac{number\ of\ desired\ outcomes}{number\ of\ total\ outcomes} = \frac{18}{12+18+18+24} = \frac{18}{72} = \frac{1}{4}$

15) Choice D is correct

1 feet $= 12$ inches: We place it in the equation

$\frac{6\ feet, 8\ inches}{4} + \frac{3feet+4\ inches}{2} = \frac{6\times12\ inches+8\ inches}{4} + \frac{3\times12\ inches+4\ inches}{2} = \frac{72\ inches+8\ inches}{4} +$
$\frac{36\ inches+4\ imches}{2} = \frac{80\ inches}{4} + \frac{40\ inches}{2} = \frac{80\ inches+80\ inches}{4} = \frac{160\ inches}{4} = 40$ inches

16) Choice C is correct

15% are registered in basketball, so we have to find 15% of 15480:

$15,480 \times 0.15 = 2,322$

17) Choice C is correct

Only choice C is equal to 120.

$\left(\left(\frac{30}{4} + \frac{13}{2}\right) \times 7\right) - \frac{11}{2} + \frac{110}{4} = \left(\left(\frac{30+26}{4}\right) \times 7\right) - \frac{11}{2} + \frac{55}{2} = \left(\left(\frac{56}{4}\right) \times 7\right) + \frac{55-11}{2} = (14 \times 7) +$
$\frac{44}{2} = 98 + 22 = 120$

18) Choice B is correct

$$\frac{5}{8} \div \frac{5}{32} = \frac{5}{8} \times \frac{32}{5} = \frac{32}{8} = 4$$

19) Choice A is correct

Let x be the number, then:

$$x^2 + 10 = 35 \rightarrow x^2 = 25 \rightarrow x^2 - 25 = 0 \rightarrow (x+5)(x-5) = 0 \rightarrow x = 5 \; or \; x = -5$$

20) Choice C is correct

The symbol $\cap$ stands for intersection. The intersection of two or more sets is the set of common elements to both sets. In this case, the common elements are $3, 8$ and 12.

21) Choice A is correct

To find the number of possible outfit combinations, multiply number of options for each factor: $6 \times 3 \times 5 = 90$

22) Choice C is correct

Compare the fractions: $(\frac{1}{5})^2 = \frac{1}{25} \rightarrow \frac{1}{25} < \frac{1}{5}$

23) Choice B is correct

The reciprocal of a fraction is the fraction reversed. To find the answer, each of the options must be considered. Choice A: The inverse of 2^3 is equal to $\frac{1}{2^3}$. Choice B must be renamed: $1\frac{1}{4} = \frac{5}{4}$. The inverse of this fraction is $\frac{4}{5}$. In the Choice C, the inverse of 3^{10} is equal to 3^{-10}. In the last option, we rename the fraction: $2\frac{2}{3} = \frac{8}{3}$. The inverse of this fraction is equal to $\frac{3}{8}$

24) Choice B is correct

$y = 4ab + 3b^3$, Plug in the values of a and b in the equation: $a = 2$ and $b = 3$

$$y = 4\,(2)\,(3) + 3\,(3)^3 = 24 + 3(27) = 24 + 81 = 105$$

25) Choice D is correct

The total number of degrees in a circle is 360. $AOB = BOD \rightarrow 20° + 20° = 40°$. $40°$ of $360°$ is $\frac{40}{360}$ which reduces to $\frac{1}{9}$.

26) Choice C is correct

$$x + 3x - 10 = \left(2 \times \left(\frac{3}{2}x + y\right)\right) - 15 \rightarrow 4x - 10 = \left(2 \times \frac{3}{2}x\right) + 2y - 15 \rightarrow 4x - 10 = 3x +$$

$$2y - 15 \rightarrow 4x - 3x - 2y = 10 - 15 \rightarrow x - 2y = -5$$

27) Choice C is correct

Check each choice:

A. $(3 \times 10^2) + (5 \times 10^2) + (45 \times 10) = 300 + 500 + 450 = 1,250$

B. $(3 \times 10^3) + (5 \times 10) + (4 \times 10) + 5 = 3000 + 50 + 40 + 5 = 3,095$

C. $(3 \times 10^3) + (5 \times 10^2) + (4 \times 10) + 5 = 3000 + 500 + 40 + 5 = 3,545$

D. $(3 \times 10^3) + (5 \times 10^2) + (45 \times 10) = 3000 + 500 + 450 = 3,950$

28) Choice D is correct

121 is not prime number, it is divided by 11.

29) Choice B is correct

$1\ m = 100\ cm \rightarrow$ The width of box in centimeters equals $100 + 33 = 133\ cm$. Convert centimeters to millimeters: $1\ cm = 10\ mm \rightarrow 133\ cm = 133 \times 10 = 1,330\ mm$.

30) Choice A is correct

Weight of the blue book$= \frac{80}{0.4} = 200\ g$, Weight of the white book$= \frac{200}{1.25} = 160\ g$

Weight of all three books: $80 + 200 + 160 = 400g$

31) Choice D is correct

Since, each of the x students in a team may invite up to 5 friends, the maximum number of people in the party is 6 times x or $6x$. ($one\ student + 5\ friends\ =\ 6\ people$)

32) Choice C is correct

Perimeter$= 2\pi r = 2 \times \pi \times \frac{20}{2} = 20 \approx 62.8 \approx 63$

33) Choice B is correct

$60\ minutes\ = 1 Hours \rightarrow \frac{270}{60} = 4.5\ hours$

34) Choice D is correct

One meter is equal to 100 centimeters, so the width of the rectangle is 200 centimeters and its length is 400 centimeters. Then: $200 \times 400 = 80,000\ cm^2$

35) Choice C is correct

R is an odd number. Let's choose 1 and 3 for R. Now, let's review the choices provided:

A. $\frac{R}{2} = \frac{1}{2} = 0.5, \frac{R}{2} = \frac{3}{2} = 1.5$, Both results are not even.

B. $R^2 = 1^2 = 1, R^2 = 3^2 = 9$, Both results are odd.

C. $1 + R = 1 + 1 = 2, 1 + R = 1 + 3 = 4$, Both results are even.

D. $3R = 3 \times 1 = 3, 3R = 3 \times 3 = 9$, One result is even and the other one is odd.

36) Choice B is correct

Average speed: $\frac{340}{8} = 42.5$ miles per hour

37) Choice B is correct

According to the figure, the radius of the bigger circle is equal to 6. First, we get the total area of the circle: $\pi r^2 \rightarrow 3 \times 6^2 = 3 \times 36 = 108$. Then, we get the area of the shaded part with a radius of 3: $\pi r^2 = 3 \times 3^2 = 27$. Now, subtract the area of the shaded area from the total area of the circle to obtain the area of the none-shaded area: $108 - 27 = 81$

38) Choice D is correct

$218{,}210 = 2.1821 \times 10^5$

39) Choice A is correct

Area of a triangle $= \dfrac{1}{2} \times$ base $\times$ height

$$50 = \frac{1}{2} \times x \times 4x \rightarrow 50 = 2x^2 \rightarrow \frac{50}{2} = \frac{2x^2}{2} \rightarrow 25 = x^2 \rightarrow x = 5$$

40) Choice D is correct

Probability is determined by dividing the number of incidences of a specific outcome (in this case rolling an even number, or rolling 2, 4 or 6) by the total number of outcomes:

$$probability = \frac{3}{6} = \frac{1}{2}$$

41) Choice C is correct

Total number of cards after removing the kings from a standard deck $= 52 - 4 = 48$

Total number of red 3 cards $= 2$

Probability of selecting a red 3 $= \dfrac{2}{48} = \dfrac{1}{24}$

42) Choice A is correct

The greatest even multiple odd 11 less than 80 is 66 (number 77 is odd) and the least odd multiple of 9 greater than 30 is 45. Then: $x + y = 66 + 45 = 111$

43) Choice A is correct

The millions begin with the seventh digit to the left of the decimal place. Because we need 153 million, we can immediately eliminate choices A. Our next three digits: 857 thousand. And the last three digits: 432, only choice A has such features.

44) Choice C is correct

Put the values of x and y in each choice provided:

A. $y = x + 4 \rightarrow y = -2 + 4 = 2$

B. $y = -x \rightarrow y = -(-2) = 2$

C. $y = 3 + x \rightarrow 3 + (-2) = 1$. This cannot be the equation of line A.

D. $y = \frac{1}{2}x + 3 \rightarrow y = \frac{1}{2} \times (-2) + 3 = -1 + 3 = 2$

45) Choice D is correct

$4x + 2 - \left(4x - \frac{1}{2}\right) = 4x + 2 - 4x + \frac{1}{2} = 2 + \frac{1}{2} = \frac{4+1}{2} = \frac{5}{2} = 2.5$

46) Choice B is correct

The sum of supplement angles is 180. Let x be that angle. Therefore, $x + 5x = 180, 6x = 180$, divide both sides by 6: $x = 30$

47) Choice D is correct

Smallest 4–digit number is 1,000, and biggest 4–digit number is 9,999. The difference is: 8,999

ISEE Middle LEVEL Math Practice Test 2 Section 1

1) Choice C is correct

$\frac{1}{6} \approx 0.16; \frac{1}{3} \approx 0.33; \frac{2}{5} = 0.4; \frac{3}{4} = 0.75$

2) Choice B is correct

$\sqrt{2(4^2) + 2(5^2) + 2(3^2)} = \sqrt{2(16) + 2(25) + 2(9)} = \sqrt{32 + 50 + 18} = \sqrt{100} = 10$. So choice B is correct.

3) Choice C is correct

Calculate each choice to find the correct answer:

A. $6t - \frac{3}{2}t \rightarrow \frac{2 \times (6t) - 3t}{2} = \frac{12t - 3t}{2} = \frac{9}{2}t$. Can't be true.

B. $\frac{5}{2}t + 3t \rightarrow \frac{5t + (3t)2}{2} = \frac{5t + 6t}{2} = \frac{11}{2}t$. Can't be true.

C. $3t \cdot \frac{5}{2}t \rightarrow 3t \times \frac{5}{2}t = \frac{15}{2}t^2$. This can be true.

D. $\frac{5}{2}t \div 3t \rightarrow \frac{\frac{5}{2}t}{3t} = \frac{5}{2}t \times \frac{1}{3}t = \frac{5}{6}t^2$. Can't be true.

4) Choice B is correct

Use the formula for Percent of Change: $\frac{\text{New Value} - \text{Old Value}}{\text{Old Value}} \times 100\%$

$\frac{28 - 40}{40} \times 100\% = -30\%$ (negative sign here means that the new price is less than old price)

5) Choice C is correct

$2f = 2 \times (2x - 3y) = 4x - 6y, \quad 2f + g = 4x - 6y + x + 4y = 5x - 2y$

6) Choice A is correct

Use the mean formula: $\frac{\text{sum of the values}}{\text{number of values}} \rightarrow \frac{20+20+30+30+40+40+40+40+50+60+60+A}{12} = 41 \rightarrow 430 + A = 41 \times 12 \rightarrow A = 492 - 430 = 62$

7) Choice B is correct

Using the Pythagorean relation, the third side of the triangle is equal to:

$\rightarrow a^2 + b^2 = c^2 \rightarrow 6^2 + 8^2 = (AC)^2 \rightarrow 36 + 64 = 100 = (AC)^2 \rightarrow AC = 10$

Distance Lisa walked: $\rightarrow AB + BC + BC = 6 + 8 + 8 = 22$

the ratio of the distance traveled to the circumference of the triangle: $\rightarrow \frac{22}{10+6+8} = \frac{22}{24} = \frac{11}{12}$

8) Choice A is correct

If the score of Mia was 60, therefore the score of Ava is 30. Since, the score of Emma was half as that of Ava, therefore, the score of Emma is 15.

9) Choice B is correct

Use the formula of areas of circles. $Area\ of\ a\ circle = \pi r^2 \Rightarrow 64\ \pi = \pi r^2 \Rightarrow 64 = r^2 \Rightarrow r = 8$, Radius of the circle is 8. Now, use the circumference formula: Circumference $= 2\pi r = 2\pi\ (8) = 16\ \pi$

10) Choice C is correct

$1.12 = \frac{112}{100}$ and $7.2 = \frac{72}{10} \rightarrow 1.12 \times 7.2 = \frac{112}{100} \times \frac{72}{10} = \frac{8,064}{1,000} = 8.064$

11) Choice C is correct

A regular pentagon has 5 equal sides. Two feet is equal to 24 inches, since the sum of lengths of four sides is 24 inches, each side measures:

$24 \div 4 = 6$ inches. The perimeter of the pentagon is: $\rightarrow 6 \times 5 = 30$ inches

12) Choice D is correct

Let x be the number. Write the equation and solve for x. $\frac{2}{3} \times 18 = \frac{2}{5} \times x \Rightarrow \frac{2 \times 18}{3} = \frac{2x}{5}$, use cross multiplication to solve for x. $5 \times 36 = 2x \times 3 \Rightarrow 180 = 6x \Rightarrow x = 30$

13) Choice C is correct

Add the first 5 numbers. $40 + 45 + 50 + 35 + 65 = 235$

To find the distance traveled in the next 5 hours, multiply the average by number of hours.

$Distance = Average \times Rate = 50 \times 5 = 250$, Add both numbers. $250 + 235 = 485$

14) Choice D is correct

$Mean = \frac{9 + 12 + 29 + 36 + 45 + 63 + 99 + 123}{8} = \frac{416}{8} = 52$

15) Choice A is correct

There are 35 marbles that are not white and 35 that are white, this makes 35 favorable outcomes to 70 total numbers of outcomes: $\frac{35}{70} = \frac{35 \div 35}{70 \div 35} = \frac{1}{2}$ or 1 to 2.

16) Choice D is correct

Let x be the original price. If the price of a laptop is decreased by 10% to $360, then: 90% of $x = 360 \Rightarrow 0.90x = 360 \Rightarrow x = 360 \div 0.90 = 400$

17) Choice B is correct

$\frac{2}{5}$ of $120 = \frac{2}{5} \times 120 = 48, \frac{1}{4}$ of $48 = \frac{1}{4} \times 48 = 12$

18) Choice C is correct

The ratio of boy to girls is 4: 7. Therefore, there are 4 boys out of 11 students. To find the answer, first divide the total number of students by 11, then multiply the result by 4.

$66 \div 11 = 6 \Rightarrow 6 \times 4 = 24$, There are 24 boys and 42 $(66 - 24)$ girls. So, 18 more boys should be enrolled to make the ratio 1: 1

19) Choice C is correct

Let's put the values of h in the choices:

A. $h = 1 \rightarrow v = 1 + 7 = 8$

$h = 2 \rightarrow v = 2 + 7 = 9 \rightarrow$ it cannot be true

B. $h = 1 \rightarrow v = 8 \times 1 = 8$

$h = 2 \rightarrow v = 8 \times 2 = 16 \rightarrow$ it cannot be true

D. $h = 1 \rightarrow v = (10 \times 1) - 2 = 8$

$h = 2 \rightarrow v = (10 \times 2) - 2 = 18 \rightarrow$ it cannot be true

Therefore, only choice C is correct.

20) Choice C is correct

Let x be the sales profit. Then, 2% of sales profit is $0.02x$. Employee's revenue: $0.02x + 5,000$

21) Choice D is correct

Let's review the choices:

A. $\frac{3}{4} > 0.8$ $\quad$ This is not a correct statement. Because $\frac{3}{4} = 0.75$ and it's less than 0.8.

B. $10\% = \frac{2}{5}$ $\quad$ This is not a correct statement. Because $10\% = 0.1$ and $\frac{2}{5} = 0.4$

C. $3 < \frac{5}{2}$ $\quad$ This is not a correct statement. Because $\frac{5}{2} = 2.5$ and it's less than 3.

D. $\frac{5}{6} > 0.8$ $\quad$ This is a correct statement. $\frac{5}{6} = 0.83 \rightarrow 0.8 < \frac{5}{6}$

22) Choice B is correct

$x = 20 + 125 = 145$

23) Choice D is correct

$\frac{3}{4} \times 80 = 60$ historical books. $80 - 60 = 20$ literary books. If historical books become doubled, their number becomes: $60 \times 2 = 120$ historical books

$20 - 10 = 10$ literary books. This means that the proportion of literary books to total number of books in the library will be: $10: (120 + 10)$ or $10: 130$, which can be reduced to $1: 13$

24) Choice B is correct

First, calculate Anna's savings in 33 weeks, then calculate Anna's savings in 33 week. Subtract the second amount from the first amount.

$(\$15.78 \times 33) - (\$14.03 \times 33) = 33 \times (\$15.78 - \$14.03) = 33 \times \$1.75 = \$57.75$

25) Choice A is correct

Petrol of car A in $250km = \frac{8\times250}{100} = 20$, Petrol of car B in $250km = \frac{6\times250}{100} = 15$, $20 - 15 = 5$

26) Choice B is correct.

The midrange of the data set is the mean of its least and greatest elements. The midrange of the first data set is: $30 - 5 = 25$. The midrange of the second data set is: $50 - 10 = 40$. So, quantity B is greater.

27) Choice B is correct.

Column A: The value of x when $y = 12$:

$y = -4x - 8 \rightarrow 12 = -4x - 8 \rightarrow -4x = 20 \rightarrow x = -5$

Column B: -4 ; -4 is greater than -5.

28) Choice C is correct.

$AB = BC = CD \rightarrow AC = AB + BC = 2BC, BD = BC + CD = 2BC$. Therefore $AC = BD$. The two quantities are equal.

29) Choice B is correct.

Let's x be as Monica's savings, and y be Jennifer's saving and z be Sandra's saving. Then: $x = \frac{7}{8}y, z = \frac{5}{4}x \rightarrow z = \frac{5}{4} \times \frac{7}{8}y \rightarrow z = \frac{35}{32}y = 1\frac{3}{32}y > y > \frac{7}{8}y$.

30) Choice B is correct.

Column A: $5t + 4t + 3t - 2t = (5 + 4 + 3 - 2)t = 10t$. Column B: $7t + 5t + 2t = (7 + 5 + 2)t = 14t$, which is greater quantity than column A.

31) Choice B is correct

Area of the triangle $= \frac{1}{2} \times 2 \times 10 = 10$

Four times the area of square $= 4 \times (2 \times 2) = 4 \times 4 = 16$. Quantity B is greater.

32) Choice D is correct.

Choose different values for x and find the value of quantity A.

$x = 1$, then:

Quantity A: $\frac{1}{x} + x = \frac{1}{1} + 1 = 2$

Quantity B is greater

$x = 10$, then: Quantity A: $\frac{1}{x} + x = \frac{1}{10} + 10 = 10\frac{1}{10}$. So, Quantity A is greater.

The relationship cannot be determined from the information given.

33) Choice D is correct.

Simply change the fractions to decimals. $\frac{4}{5} = 0.80, \frac{6}{7} = 0.857 ..., \frac{5}{6} = 0.8333 ...$

As you can see, x lies between 0.80 and 0.857... and it can be 0.81 or 0.84. The first one is less than 0.833... and the second one is greater than 0.833... . The relationship cannot be determined from the information given.

34) Choice A is correct.

Simplify quantity B. Quantity B: $(\frac{x}{6})^6 = \frac{x^6}{6^6}$

Since, the two quantities have the same numerator (x^6) and the denominator in quantity B is bigger $(6^6 > 6)$, then the quantity A is greater.

35) Choice A is correct

Quantity A: If there are 13 marbles in the basket, 3 of them are blue. Therefore, quantity A is 6 and quantity B is 5. If you choose other values for the blue and black marbles, you will get the same result.

36) Choice C is correct

Since A_1 is equal to $60°$ and $AB = AC$, then $\angle B = \angle C_1 = 60° \rightarrow \angle C_2 = 180 - 60 = 120$. $\angle D = \angle A_2 = \frac{120°}{2} = 60°$. So, $\angle B = \angle D = 60°$.

37) Choice A is correct

$2x^3 + 10 = 64 \rightarrow 2x^3 = 64 - 10 = 54 \rightarrow x^3 = \frac{54}{2} = 27 \rightarrow x = \sqrt[3]{27} = \sqrt[3]{3^3} = 3$

$120 - 18y = 84 \rightarrow -18y = 84 - 120 = -36 \rightarrow y = \frac{-36}{-18} = 2$

ISEE Middle LEVEL Math Practice Test 2 Section 2

1) Choice B is correct

15% of 180 = $\frac{15}{100} \times 180 = 27$, Let x be the number then, $x = 27 + 12 = 39$

2) Choice B is correct

Number of red cars to blue cars in a parking lot is in the ratio of $2:5$ and 90 blue cars are in the parking lot. Write a proportion and solve: $\frac{2}{5} = \frac{x}{90} \rightarrow x = \frac{2 \times 90}{5} = 36$

3) Choice B is correct

$3 \times \left(\frac{1}{3} - \frac{1}{9}\right) + 1 = 3 \times \left(\frac{3-1}{9}\right) + 1 = \frac{6}{9} + 1 = \frac{2}{3} + 1 = \frac{5}{3} = 1.66$

4) Choice D is correct

Number of blue pencils $= 90 - 43 = 47$, Percent of blue pencils is: $\frac{47}{90} \times 100 = 52.2\% \approx 52\%$

5) Choice B is correct

$(x + 5)^2 = 144 \rightarrow x + 5 = \sqrt[2]{144} = \sqrt[2]{12^2} = 12 \rightarrow x = 12 - 5 = 7$ or $x + 5 = -12 \rightarrow$

$x = -17$

6) Choice D is correct

The formula for slope is: $m = \frac{y_2 - y_1}{x_2 - x_1} \rightarrow \frac{-4-(-2)}{-6-(6)} = \frac{-2}{-12} = \frac{1}{6}$. So, choice D is correct

7) Choice A is correct

The perimeter of rectangle is: $2 \times (4 + 7) = 2 \times 11 = 22$, The perimeter of circle is: $2\pi r = 2 \times 3 \times \frac{10}{2} = 30$, Difference in perimeter is: $30 - 22 = 8$

Let's simplify the equation:

$x = \frac{2y}{3} - 6$, multiply both sides of the equation by 3. Then: $x = \frac{2y}{3} - 6 \rightarrow 3x = 2y - 18$, subtract $3x$ from both sides: $3x - 3x = 2y - 3x - 18 \rightarrow 2y - 3x - 18 = 0$

All other choices are not equal to the equation provided.

8) Choice B is correct

Use this formula: Percent of Change $= \frac{New\ Value - Old\ Value}{Old\ Value} \times 100\%$

$\frac{16,000 - 20,000}{20,000} \times 100\% = -20\%$ and $\frac{12,800 - 16,000}{16,000} \times 100\% = -20\%$ (negative sign simply means the value of the car decreases)

9) Choice C is correct

Let x be the number. Write the equation and solve for x. $(24 - x) \div x = 3$, Multiply both sides by x. $(24 - x) = 3x$, then add x both sides. $24 = 4x$, now divide both sides by 4. $x = 6$

10) Choice B is correct

Only choice B is correct. $\left(\frac{10}{3} \times 27\right) + \left(\frac{5}{2} \times 2\right) = 90 + 5 = 95$

11) Choice A is correct

If $\frac{3x}{2} = 60$, then $3x = 120 \rightarrow x = 40$, $\frac{2x}{5} = \frac{2 \times 40}{5} = \frac{80}{5} = 16$

12) Choice C is correct

$\frac{1}{3} = 0.33$; $\frac{7}{9} = 0.77$; $85\% = 0.85$

13) Choice B is correct

$Surface\ Area\ of\ a\ cube = 6s^2 = 150 \rightarrow s^2 = \frac{150}{6} = 25 \rightarrow s = 5$. One side of the cube is $5\ cm$. Then, the volume of the cube is: $Volume\ of\ a\ cube = s^3 = 5^3 = 125\ cm^3$

14) Choice D is correct

A. $3^3 = 27 \neq 30$

B. $4^3 = 64 \neq 84$

C. $5^3 = 125 \neq 130$

D. $6^3 = 216$

15) Choice D is correct

Find the difference of each pairs of numbers: $2, 3, 5, 8, 12, 17, 23, \_\_, 38$

The difference of 2 and 3 is 1, 3 and 5 is 2, 5 and 8 is 3, 8 and 12 is 4, 12 and 17 is 5, 17 and 23 is 6, 23 and next number should be 7. The number is $23 + 7 = 30$

16) Choice D is correct

z is the intersection of the three circles. Therefore, it must be even (from circle A), a perfect square (from circle B), and a multiple of 10 (from circle C).

From the choices, only 100 is even, perfect square and multiple of 10.

17) Choice C is correct

$0.45 + 0.3 + 2.6 + 2.94 = 6.29$

18) Choice D is correct

12 hours $= 720$ minutes $\rightarrow \frac{45}{1} = \frac{720}{x} \rightarrow x = \frac{720}{45} = 16.$

19) Choice C is correct.

A graph represents y as a function of x if

$$x_1 = x_2 \rightarrow y_1 = y_2$$

In choice C, for each x, we have two different values for y.

20) Choice A is correct

$13 < -3x - 2 < 22 \rightarrow$ Add 2 to all sides. $13 + 2 < -3x - 2 + 2 < 22 + 2$

$\rightarrow 15 < -3x < 24 \rightarrow$ Divide all sides by -3. (Remember that when you divide all sides of an inequality by a negative number, the inequality sing will be swapped. < becomes >)

$\frac{15}{-3} > \frac{-3x}{-3} > \frac{24}{-3}.$ $-8 < x < -5$

21) Choice B is correct

Number of biology book: 35. Total number of books; $35 + 95 + 80 = 210$

The ratio of the number of biology books to the total number of books is: $\frac{35}{210} = \frac{1}{6}$

22) Choice B is correct

$$60 \; minutes = 1 Hours \rightarrow \frac{185}{60} = 3.08 \; Hours$$

23) Choice C is correct

First, simplify the equation: $2x - 12 + 4 = 4y \rightarrow 2x - 8 = 4y$. Subtract $2x$ from both sides of the equation: $2x - 2x - 8 = 4y - 2x \rightarrow -8 = 4y - 2x$. Divide both sides by 2. Then: $-8 = 4y - 2x \rightarrow -4 = 2y - x$

24) Choice D is correct

57 is not prime number, it is divisible by 3 and 19.

25) Choice C is correct

The area of the square is 64 inches. Therefore, the side of the square is square root of the area. $\sqrt{64} = 8$ inches, four times the side of the square is the perimeter: $4 \times 8 = 32 \; inches$

26) Choice C is correct

Each cube has 8 faces, so by dividing the area of the cube by 8, area of each face is obtained: $150 \div 8 = 25$. Therefore, each side becomes 5.

volume of the cube$= 5 \times 5 \times 5 = 125$

27) Choice B is correct

Because ABC and ADE are similar, their corresponding sides are in the same proportions.

$\frac{AB}{AE} = \frac{AC}{AD} = \frac{BC}{DE}$

28) Choice C is correct

Sandra finished the study in $10\ hr.\ 30\ min + 2\ hr.\ 45\ min = 12\ hr.\ 75\ min\ A.M.$

There are 60 minutes in an hour. Then: $12\ hr.\ 75\ min = 13\ hr.\ 15\ min = 1\ hr.\ 15\ min\ P.M.$

Sandra went shopping in $1\ hr.\ 15\ min + 1\ hr.\ 35\ min = 2\ hr.\ 50\ min.$

Sandra went shopping at: $2:50$

29) Choice A is correct

The width of a rectangle is $4x$ and its length is $6x$. Therefore, the perimeter of the rectangle is $20x$. $Perimeter\ of\ a\ rectangle = 2(width + length) = 2(4x + 6x) = 2(10x) = 20x$

The perimeter of the rectangle is 80. Then: $20x = 80 \rightarrow x = 4$

30) Choice C is correct

The distance between Jason and Joe is 9 miles. Jason running at 5.5 miles per hour and Joe is running at the speed of 7 miles per hour. Therefore, every hour the distance is 1.5 miles less.

$9 \div 1.5 = 6$

31) Choice D is correct

Use PEMDAS (order of operation):

$[5 \times (-14) + 8] - (-4) + [4 \times 5] \div 2 = [-70 + 8] - (-4) + [20] \div 2 = [-70 + 8] - (-4) + 10 = [-62] - (-4) + 10 = [-62] + 4 + 10 = -48$

32) Choice C is correct

In choice C, the digit 2 has a value of $2 \times 10,000 = (2 \times 10^4)$

33) Choice D is correct

If the inverse of the number is multiplied by the number, the answer is 1.

A. $6 \times (-6) = -36$

B. $5 \times 6 = 30$

C. $5 \times \left(-\frac{1}{5}\right) = -1$

D. $1 \times 1 = 1$

34) Choice B is correct

Since the point is in quarter III, x-coordinate must be positive and y-coordinates must be negative. Therefore, only choice B can be correct.

35) Choice C is correct

A quadrilateral with two pairs of parallel sides without a right angle could be a parallelogram.

36) Choice A is correct

In the figure angle A is labeled $(6x - 12)$ and it measures 42. Thus, $(6x - 12) = 42$ and $6x = 54$ or $x = 9$.

That means that angle B, which is labeled $(9x + 6)$, must measure $9 \times 9 + 6 = 87$.

Since the three angles of a triangle must add up to 180,

$42 + 87 + y + 11 = 180$, then: $y + 140 = 180 \rightarrow y = 180 - 140$

37) Choice A is correct

The two triangles are similar. So, set up a proportion to solve for x: $\frac{10+x}{x} = \frac{4}{2} \rightarrow 2 \times (10 + x) = 4x \rightarrow 20 + 2x = 4x \rightarrow 20 = 2x \rightarrow x = 10$. The area of smaller triangle (shaded part) is: $\frac{1}{2} \times 2 \times 10 = 10$

38) Choice B is correct

Calculate each equation: $(A) = \frac{8 \times 4}{2} = \frac{32}{2} = 16, (B) = 2^3 = 2 \times 2 \times 2 = 8,$

$(C) = (2 \times 3) + 2 = 6 + 2 = 8 \rightarrow (B) = (C) = 8 \rightarrow (B) + (C) = 8 + 8 = 16 \rightarrow$

$(B) + (C) = (A) \rightarrow$ So, choice B is correct.

39) Choice B is correct

$1,269 = 6^4; \rightarrow 6^x = 6^4 \rightarrow x = 4$

40) Choice B is correct

The area of trapezoid is: $\left(\frac{9+11}{2}\right) \times 5 = 50$

41) Choice D is correct

$12.124 \div 0.002 = \dfrac{\frac{12,124}{1,000}}{\frac{2}{1,000}} = \dfrac{12,124}{2} = 6,062$

42) Choice A is correct

$AD = 50, AB = CD = 20 \rightarrow AB + BC + CD = AD \rightarrow 20 + BC + 20 = 50 \rightarrow 40 + BC = 50 \rightarrow BC = 50 - 40 = 10$

43) Choice B is correct

$18 - 12.49 = \$5.51$

44) Choice D is correct

Write the equation and solve for B: $0.60A = 0.20B$, divide both sides by 0.20, then you will have $\frac{0.60}{0.20}A = B$, therefore: $B = 3A$, and B is 3 times of A or it's 300% of A.

45) Choice B is correct

The probability of choosing a Hearts is $\frac{13}{52} = \frac{1}{4}$

46) Choice C is correct

$$\frac{3}{4} + \frac{\frac{-2}{5}}{\frac{4}{10}} = \frac{3}{4} + \frac{(-2) \times 10}{5 \times 4} = \frac{3}{4} + \frac{-20}{20} = \frac{3}{4} - 1 = \frac{3 - 4}{4} = -\frac{1}{4}$$

47) Choice D is correct

Donna's equation: $3\frac{1}{3} = \frac{10}{3} = \frac{30}{9} \neq \frac{10}{9}$, Anna's equation: $12.5 = \frac{125}{10} \neq \frac{125}{100} = 1.25$

Receive the PDF version of this book or get another FREE book!

Thank you for using our Book!

Do you LOVE this book?

Then, you can get the PDF version of this book or another book absolutely FREE!

Please email us at:

info@EffortlessMath.com

for details.

Author's Final Note

I hope you enjoyed reading this book. You've made it through the book! Great job!

First of all, thank you for purchasing this practice book. I know you could have picked any number of books to help you prepare for your ISEE Middle Level Math test, but you picked this book and for that I am extremely grateful.

It took me years to write this workbook for the ISEE Middle Level Math because I wanted to prepare a comprehensive ISEE Middle Level Math workbook to help test takers make the most effective use of their valuable time while preparing for the test.

After teaching and tutoring math courses for over a decade, I've gathered my personal notes and lessons to develop this practice book. It is my greatest hope that the exercises in this book could help you prepare for your test successfully.

If you have any questions, please contact me at reza@effortlessmath.com and I will be glad to assist. Your feedback will help me to greatly improve the quality of my books in the future and make this book even better. Furthermore, I expect that I have made a few minor errors somewhere in this book. If you think this to be the case, please let me know so I can fix the issue as soon as possible.

If you enjoyed this book and found some benefit in reading this, I'd like to hear from you and hope that you could take a quick minute to post a review on the book's Amazon page. To leave your valuable feedback, please visit: amzn.to/3BWmkC7

Or scan this QR code.

I personally go over every single review, to make sure my books really are reaching out and helping students and test takers. Please help me help ISEE Middle Level Math test takers, by leaving a review!

I wish you all the best in your future success!

Reza Nazari

Math teacher and author

CPSIA information can be obtained
at www.ICGtesting.com
Printed in the USA
LVHW051040141222
735223LV00013B/396